Balboa

SWORDSMAN AND CONQUISTADOR

In 1513 Vasco Núñez de Balboa first sighted the blue waters of the Pacific Ocean, a discovery that changed the maps of the world and the course of history.

Here is an authentic biography of this great explorer. Not only was he an outstanding colonizer and military strategist, as well as the most formidable swordsman of the early sixteenth century, but he was a noble, kindly man—rare qualities in those days when white conquistadors were generally brutal taskmasters. In bringing this remarkable man to life, Felix Riesenberg, Jr. vividly recreates Balboa's early days as a page boy in the household of a noble, his brilliant swordfights, his shipwrecks, battles and intrigues.

BALBOA

Swordsman
&
Conquistador

by FELIX RIESENBERG, Jr.
illustrated by FEDOR ROJANKOVSKY
RANDOM HOUSE · NEW YORK

To my Great Aunt

Adele Guye Riesenberg

CONTENTS

Foreword

The life of Vasco Núñez de Balboa, discoverer of the Pacific Ocean, is a story of adventure which needs no polishing by any writer. But it is true that great jealousy and iron censorship partly succeeded in erasing much of the man's past.

In this book I have adhered to the known facts except in the following incidents: the opening sword fight, which is faithful to the period although the exact time and setting are of my own invention; and the Moorish War, when Balboa gains experience in combat and receives instruction from Juan Perez, a mythical soldier of Spain. I have used these scenes for characterization and to explain how it was possible for Balboa to have reached the age of thirty-five, in the very roughest of company, unmarked by sword or fist. Present-day authorities confirm that to have done so a man would have needed some prize tricks in addition to an exceptional physique.

Incidents at Hispaniola and Panama, all based on documented history, have been simplified somewhat and dramatized. This has been done not only to make for better reading but to point up the courage and resourcefulness needed to make the great discovery which remains unique in the history of mankind.

For whatever it may mean to this story I will note that at the age of twelve I was aboard my father's sailing ship which anchored in the Rio Tinto, just below the ancient Spanish city of Moguer where young Balboa began his education. On that voyage we sailed homeward from Cadiz, touching at the Canary Islands, then running before the northeast trades in the wake of the discoverer. In my teens I voyaged as a sailor in the Caribbean and through the Panama Canal. And recently—as though to complete some cycle—I was again in the West Indies, this time with my twelve-year-old son.

FELIX RIESENBERG, JR.

Balboa

SWORDSMAN AND CONQUISTADOR

1

The Swordsman

Late on a September afternoon in the year 1491 a tall, strongly-made boy began to slow his ambling pace along a dusty highway. He frowned slightly as he listened to some distant sound. Then he sighted five miles ahead, across rolling hills, to the castle tower above the ancient Spanish city of Moguer. There lay home and safety. He gripped the hilt of a long sword with a hand that was surprisingly large and muscular for a boy of sixteen. The other hand brushed through blond, reddish hair and he slowed his pace even more while his head bent in concentration. His frown deepened.

Trailing the big boy, responsible for his idle walk and concern, came five ragged youngsters not quite in their teens. They were footsore and weary after an eighty-mile march from their home town of Jerez de los Caballeros in the mountains of southwestern Spain. Soon they hoped to be safe in the castle that lay ahead, ready to begin their education as pages to Don Pedro Puertocarrero, the deaf Lord of Moguer.

In those days the castle of some renowned warrior was a boarding school where boys destined for a career of arms were sent if their families could secure an appointment. Other boys might be apprenticed to their fathers' trades, or go to sea, but these future military captains of Spain were to be given five years of training as pages. After they had passed all tests they would be esquires like the boy with the sword —almost full-fledged fighting men.

All that week the new pages-to-be had seen wondrous and frightening things including the body of a beggar who had been murdered for his few coppers. The highways were dangerous, even in daytime, for at the end of the fifteenth century there were great poverty and fear throughout Europe.

On the journey down to the Spanish-Atlantic sea-coast the little party had been in the company of soldiers. Now, for the last few miles, they were without escort, and all knew the risk that lay in traveling the Seville Road which curved close to the river towns of Palos, Huelva and Moguer. Not far away thrived the wild seaport of Sanlucar de Barrameda. Vandals lurked where the ships anchored and young boys were always snatched for use as slaves or pages. But the apprentices were not overly worried even when they saw the concern of their guardian. It was said that for all his kindness and gentle manner he could be a terror with his sword.

As the group came to a sharp bend in the highway, near a cluster of cork oaks, the boy with the sword waved the others into the shade and lifted a hand for silence.

From up ahead came the sound of hoof beats. A body of horsemen approached. The big boy now wiped sweat from his handsome face. The frown became a scowl as some inner sense warned him of danger. His hand tightened on the sword hilt.

Before the younger ones could ask questions the horses thundered close. Three riders galloped around the turn. In the lead, astride a great charger, rode a cruel-looking man of about forty who wore a black spade beard. He was dressed in rich, dark velvet and white plumes adorned his new-fashioned Italian cap. He was a noble of some sort. At sight of the boys he reined in and the ten riders behind him circled to a halt in clouds of dust. There were three lances in half armor, led by a lieutenant, along with crossbowmen and two lackeys. A single page led a pair of empty saddle horses.

The horsemen surrounded the boys, tough faces grinning down meanly. When the bearded leader had his mount under control he threw a handful of small coins down onto the ground. The future pages of Moguer scrambled to recover the coppers. The boy with the sword waited.

"Ho, redtop!" the bearded man taunted. "You have let the small ones grab the *blancas*. Or will you relieve them of their gains later?"

"I am an esquire, Excellency. The boys may keep what they rescue from the dust."

The rider's face hardened. "How old are you, redtop?"

"Seventeen my next birthday." The boy blushed with anger. "And Excellency," he added boldly, "men call me Vasco Núñez de Balboa—*not redtop.*"

The man had been about to raise his whip but now he paused. "Balboa?" he asked. "Not by chance a son of Nuno Arias de Balboa, the debtor of Jerez de los Caballeros?"

The boy's blush deepened. He controlled his anger only with an effort. "You have my father's name correct," he said. "It is true our castle was lost in a lawsuit. But we are still of noble birth—*hidalgos.*"

"Humph!" The man looked down scornfully. He shot a glance over at the small boys and his attention centered on the youngest. "Lieutenant," he said without turning in the saddle, "take those two. They will serve until we reach Lisbon."

"Hold, sir!" Balboa raised his long sword and stepped forward a pace. "These boys are to be pages to my lord, Don Pedro Puertocarrero. It is my duty to give them safe conduct to the castle."

The bearded noble raised a hand to stay the guffaws of his rough escort. He looked away from the frightened boys, his dark eyes boring down at Balboa. "I did not consult you," he rasped. "When I need two pages I am not likely to ask advice from any overgrown lout."

"Then you are likely to fight me, sir!" Balboa hefted the sword. His cool, blue-green eyes did not leave the man.

"Lieutenant!" The leader spat out the word. "Teach this pup a lesson. I want his right ear—a clean job.

And cut the tendon of his sword arm above the elbow."

"Wait!" Balboa paused to let the enemy think he was afraid. "The lieutenant is mounted," he said in apparent protest.

"Ho!" jeered the leader. "You are being punished, boy, not engaged. Or would you rather strip off that peasant shirt and take a whipping before your boys join me?"

"No," Balboa answered calmly. He raised his sword toward the lieutenant. "Why not let your champion don helmet, gorget and vambraces? Perhaps if he held a lance there would be less risk for him."

Out of the saddle came the lieutenant, a veteran of the Moorish War. He swore and glowered as he threw down his buckler and tossed away a small Spanish dagger. He beckoned to the skinny page to help him out of his breastplate. On the man's right cheek a scar stood out lividly.

Balboa breathed deeply of the warm autumn air and studied his opponent. The man was in a temper, which would help. And he himself would need every advantage. This burly fellow was an experienced man-at-arms who had probably killed any number of men in hundreds of fights. He, on the other hand, had never drawn blood outside the tilting yard. This was no game. It meant fierce combat which could leave him maimed. To lose the use of his arm forever! To go through life with a cropped ear! The thought was almost more than he could bear.

Balboa glanced at the boys huddled in a knot off the road. One smiled bravely; another tried to hide his fear with a stammered word of encouragement. The three smallest were whimpering.

The lieutenant was almost ready. Balboa watched his way of moving. He had a tough-muscled body and heavy, sloping shoulders but no greater reach or thicker wrists than his young adversary. The man's strategy, Balboa felt certain, would be to attack with tremendous force, first to disarm, then to cut him.

"Inform me, redtop," said the leader, ready to enjoy the slaughter, "what manner of sword is that toy?" He motioned the lieutenant to wait. He must have the information while it could still be given.

"It was made for me by an armorer of Toledo," Balboa said. "It was designed by my lord who has taught me the art of the sword."

"A light weapon until you are a man," the bearded noble scoffed. "What is the length? Or do you know?"

"I know very well," Balboa said absently. He had just picked up the faint sound of horses. Could a

The burly lieutenant was an experienced man-at-arms

party be coming out from Moguer? Was he to be saved before he could prove himself?

"Speak up then!" the leader ordered. "Are you suddenly mute with fear?"

"I am no verse-maker," Balboa answered, remaining cool. "My sword is three feet and six inches. It was made long for the way I have been taught to fight. But I have never heard it called a plaything."

The man's spade beard jutted up as he threw his head back to laugh. "Raul," he told his page, "in a moment you may have the plaything."

Again Balboa picked up the sound of horses. They were coming across the fields from the Rio Tinto ferry. He could now stall and avoid the fight. Instead he managed a taunt of his own. "Your lieutenant," he said evenly, "will grow into a captain if you hold him back while you make poor jests."

The lieutenant surged forward. Balboa's long sword flashed in the air and he shuffled slightly. Road dust showed the fast movement of his feet.

Angry and excited, the lieutenant pressed his attack with a cutting slash. He was confident he would force back this baby-faced esquire. The sword seemed to leap through the still, hot air.

Balboa anticipated the arc of the heavy weapon. His eyes gleamed, his lips were pressed into a grim smile. All fear left him with the start of action. His body obeyed with a coordination none of these men had ever seen. Like a panther he streaked in to parry. His thinner blade clipped across, then up. The clash of metal caused the horses to shy. One of the boys cried out in alarm.

The lieutenant's forward plunge carried him head-long into a collision with Balboa. The man jumped back, teeth bared, arm raised for another slash. This time he no longer aimed at the arm. His steely, close-set eyes were on the neck. He would teach this whelp to make him use two blows!

But Balboa moved in again instead of away. His entire system was disciplined to coolness and precision by five years of tedious practice. Great courage made him seem unaware of the sharp-edged sword that glinted less than a foot away from his head.

It now required more than ordinary bravery to carry out his next maneuver. This trick of the sword had been taught to him by wily old Don Pedro. It was a daring combination of the thrust and lunge which European masters of the fence would not perfect for another fifty years.

Balboa's right leg shot ahead, his left straightening at an angle to the road. Then, with his left arm extended directly back, his body snapped upright, and he thrust his sword forward, the tip ripping into the lieutenant's arm.

As he cried out in pain the soldier loosened his grip and his sword landed flat against Balboa's head. The useless weapon had barely clattered to the road when the lieutenant screamed a second time. With a lightning-fast thrust Balboa had laid open the man's cheek. The gushing cut would heal into a scar to match the other one.

Before the bearded noble could intervene, Balboa bounded to his side, close to the big charger. His sword whipped up, neatly skewering the flat velvet cap. A twist of the blade sent the fancy headpiece scaling in a high arc. The feather plumes steered it toward the open-mouthed boys.

"Now you, *señor!*" Balboa's flashing eyes warned the others in the noble's party not to move.

But the youthful swordsman was interrupted. The horses he had heard before the fight were already rounding the bend. Balboa recognized the heavy figure in the lead as the captain of guards from Moguer Castle.

In the dimly-lit tower room that overlooked the Rio Tinto, Don Pedro Puertocarrero sat bent in a heavy oak chair. At his side stood the friend of his childhood, the venerable Fray Juan. Stands of armor showed in the background like ghostly warriors, and swords and trophies hung on each side of a crucifix over the empty fireplace.

Faint candlelight picked out a pale spot on the old soldier's head where hair had been rubbed away by helmets in many campaigns. His keen, hawklike face was clean shaven. This was old-fashioned in the fifteenth century for at that time the younger men grew beards.

Balboa had been summoned almost immediately after his return. Now he entered the room and crossed to a high, narrow table upon which some candles stood burning. Here the deaf lord could see the faces and read the lips of those he interviewed.

"Vasco Núñez de Balboa," said the old man in a deep voice, "today you did your duty to me. You also proved what I have known for many months. You are already an *egregius digladiator,* a master of the sword, despite your youth. This much delights me."

"Thank you, my lord."

"Silence!" Don Pedro roared. "Let me finish. You are still a boy, in many ways a child. This gift of swordsmanship is partly due to the body God bestowed on you, along with great courage. But it is

"You are already a master of the sword," said Don Pedro

also due to the trick of the blade I have taught you. Your great skill, my boy, may be the end of you."

The old priest nodded sadly. He pretended not to notice the young man's discomfort.

"You will have a rougher road to travel than most," the old warrier continued. "Tonight you are a hero of sorts. But you have excited envy in many. By the week's end you will have been challenged a dozen times. Each victory will add to your list of enemies for this is a world of small-minded men."

Balboa rubbed his chin, perplexed. When he was granted leave to speak he asked: "What would you, my lord? That I had groveled before an arrogant robber? That I had cringed like a coward and let him have me whipped? And then permit him to steal two frightened children?"

The Lord of Moguer exchanged a glance with Fray Juan, then slowly shook his head. "You did your duty, my boy," he repeated less harshly. "It is what I would expect. You will always defend the smaller ones. And that, even more than your sword arm, marks you a man."

"True," said the priest. "It may be, Vasco Núñez," he added slowly, "that God has reserved you for great matters. This I feel and believe."

Don Pedro nodded and eyed the tall figure in the

candlelight. "It is unfortunate, young man," he said, "that you are not also clever. Did it occur to you to pretend fear? You might have hurried here. Rescue would have been a certainty."

Balboa shook his head as he worked his big hands behind his back. "I had no need to pretend fear," he said. "But you had been insulted, my lord. My family name had been smeared. And the boys. Could I ever face them again after any such cowardly act?"

Balboa paused and caught the sharp eye of Fray Juan. "I confess, Father," he said sheepishly, "that the bearded man's words and manner helped provoke me to the sword."

Don Pedro hid a smile with folded hands. But his manner was stern when he said: "Perhaps age will teach you to be more scheming, although I doubt that greatly. We are in a period of much trickery. For the time being we must give you some protection. Tomorrow you will depart. Your education is finished."

"My lord!" Balboa stepped forward a pace, alarm on his young face. When he had been waved back into the area of flickering light he declared: "I would rather die in a brawl than return home. There is nothing for me at Jerez de los Caballeros. Nothing but shame. On the streets this time I was taunted by old men and women. We are poor and in debt. My mother, my father, my brothers . . . First, my lord, I must make my fortune, gain gold . . ."

"Silence!" Don Pedro roared a second time, and one of the candles blew out. "Do you account me ungrateful, boy? You brought honor to me today. You have shown the new ones an example of courage. They will remember when they carry my banner."

"Pardon, my lord. I felt you were displeased."

"Nonsense! I am trying to show you the way. The safest place for you is in the field. Their Majesties are at Granada and the Alhambra will fall before the year is out. You can make no great mistakes in combat. Tomorrow you leave for war. Let your sword reason with the Moor."

2

Victory at Granada

The next morning before the castle was astir Don Pedro stepped out onto the tower battlements. Below, the medieval town loomed blue-gray in the dawn. As the first rooster crowed Don Pedro watched the opening of a heavy door. In a moment the alert figure of Balboa appeared in the courtyard. It had been thus every morning for five years.

The old man's thoughts went back to the arrival of a tall, slim boy from Jerez de los Caballeros. Don

Pedro had been delighted to take on the education of this lad, for the son of his old comrade-in-arms was a healthy specimen. Boys who survived the rugged mountain climate in the province of Estremadura grew up to be the strongest men in Europe. Another few years and young Balboa would stand three inches above six feet and weigh some two hundred pounds —a big man in any age.

The deaf lord smiled as he reviewed the education of his pupil. The boy had passed the seven chivalrous accomplishments: arms, riding, swimming, wrestling, hunting, chess and verse-making. At the last he was poor. But with the sword he excelled. Don Pedro longed for his own youth as he watched the boy disappear into the armory.

Balboa closed the door behind him and felt the first twinge of loneliness at the thought of leaving. He inhaled the familiar smell of oil, steel and leather that mixed with the stale odor of rubbing liniment and perspiration. He gazed at the armor and weapons on the far wall and hefted one of the weights he had used so often to develop his wrists. Through a barred window he could see the barrier, kennels and the mews that held the hunting falcons. After a last look he walked out to the stables. A favorite stallion whinnied. He laughed and tossed the horse a handful of hay before hurrying to the city gates.

A crooked street led down to the Ribera, the estuary, now crowded with vessels in various stages of completion. There Balboa had spent many hours working in the shipyard, for castle pages were given practical experience in whatever craft was practiced by the town.

Beyond the launching ways, and below the hills that rolled westward to nearby Palos, he could see the strip of beach where as a page he had skipped flat rocks across the water. As he daydreamed he heard his name called from the quay.

Balboa returned the hail of Francisco Nino of the famous seafaring family. Then he ran down to the fitting-out dock where the new caravel *Nina* lay alongside.

"I am sorry to hear that you leave, *amigo*," said the young sailor. "If you chose you might be able to go to sea for some real adventure. No mere expedition to eat mule meat and drink rain water at a siege."

"Adventure?" Balboa laughed. "To be cooped up in a little boat? To ferry on the Mediterranean? Or toss in the gales off Britain? Better to enter a convent, Nino."

Nino smiled tolerantly. "Wait," he said, picking

up a wooden mallet. "Soon these 'boats,' as you call the ships, will be sailing to the land of the Great Khan. You have seen that Genoese down the road at La Rabida. He is a powerful sea commander."

Balboa agreed. "Christopher Columbus looks a man. It may be true the world is round. My head refuses to be concerned right now. I must be off."

"*Adios.*"

The ringing of chapel bells and savory smells from the kitchens awaited Balboa at the castle. After a big breakfast of hot spiced milk and meat served on a slab of bread, he shook hands with many in farewell. And again he was conscious of a feeling of lonesomeness that saddened him. But the mood did not last long. Even before the spires of Moguer had dropped from sight when he rode away with his party that morning, he had regained his spirits. Adventure lay ahead!

At Seville, Balboa joined a company of lances serving under the renowned young Captain Juan Ponce de Leon. The future conqueror of Puerto Rico and discoverer of Florida was fighting at Granada. His soldiers had the latest news.

King Ferdinand and Queen Isabella had set up their court at Santa Fe outside of Granada, five miles from the famous Alhambra palace in southern Spain.

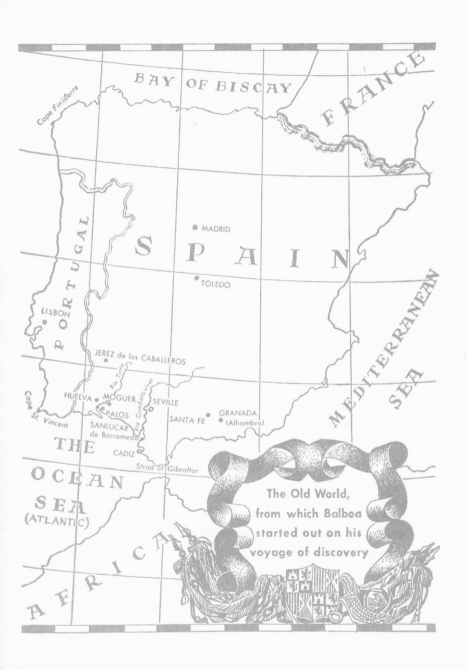

The Old World, from which Balboa started out on his voyage of discovery

Inside the walls of the besieged city a quarter of a million Moors were being starved to submission by the Spanish blockade. In a few months King Boabdil was sure to surrender.

Nearing camp, the company overtook other groups. Balboa drifted into a party composed of boys like himself. They exchanged pasts which were much the same. All had been pages and were now esquires. They burned with ambition to fight. Sons of the rich might go to the University of Salamanca to study law or medicine but these eager fellows sought honor and riches in battle. Their common fear was that they would arrive too late. They breathed more easily when the vermilion towers of Granada came into sight.

The treatment of these hopeful lads was the same then as it has always been in war. Waiting for them were the seasoned veterans—dirty, bored, underfed, and with few illusions after ten years of campaigning. The new recruits promised sport. The grisly veterans eyed the fresh young men, so well nourished and starry-eyed. Because he was tall and striking to look at, Balboa was a natural butt for their cruel jests.

"Can I wrestle?" Balboa smiled with good humor as he repeated the question. He had been taught modesty but he also knew his worth.

A square was marked off and soldiers crowded around the newcomers. Balboa stripped to the waist. Although he was well-muscled he looked like a stripling beside his opponent, whom the men called Perez.

Juan Perez, a typical veteran, was a thick-set man with a bullet-like head set on a neck that seemed part of his huge, hairy shoulders. His face was scarred and his flattened nose gave evidence of the many times it had been broken.

Balboa and Perez, crouched and with arms bent, circled each other slowly. The man was half a head shorter than Balboa but of tremendous breadth. For a moment the boy wondered if the marred features told of stupidity. Yet he must be careful. He had been warned never to judge by looks alone, nor by the manner in which men spoke.

Suddenly the two locked arms. Then Perez jerked away and cuffed Balboa on the right ear. The veterans cheered; a few *hidalgos* protested. The ringing blow made Balboa lose his temper. He would show this fellow!

When Perez feinted to kick, Balboa's big hands were ready to grasp the right ankle and whirl the soldier into the arms of his jeering friends. But before he could even bend the boy felt an agonizing blow reach his upper lip. For an instant he was paralyzed. Then a sharp punch toppled him and knocked him unconscious. The fight had lasted less than a minute.

The days which followed would have been intolerable at Moguer. But here among fifty thousand troops Balboa was a nobody. And life for soldiers at a siege was busy. All captains feared boredom far more than battle so there was constant drilling, riding and lookout duty. At every free moment there were tilts and contests.

Swordsmen from England, France and Italy were at Santa Fe to test their skill and learn the latest cuts and thrusts. In these engagements Balboa regained most of his self-esteem. And with sword in hand he never lost his temper.

After defeating other young esquires he was matched higher and higher. Among the captains who came to see this big, blond swordsman was Juan Ponce de Leon who would remember and a few years later call on Balboa. There on the field before Granada, too, were the first of Spain's great "Captains of Compliments," founders of the world's foremost school of fencing. Recognizing a natural fighter of heroic stature, they were anxious to have him test their theories on swordplay.

Also at the fights was Juan Perez who wagered

heavily on Balboa and tried awkwardly to be friends. Like the other men-at-arms, Perez had been impressed by the way this young *hidalgo* had accepted his beating in the wrestling match. Many castle-trained boys, filled with ideas of chivalry, would have complained to their commanders.

"We men-at-arms like you, *compañero*," Perez said one night when they were alone on lookout duty. "You have something the other gentlemen lack . . . men will always follow you. Now, I would like to do you a favor."

Balboa was about to object. Then he recalled one of the proverbs he had so laboriously copied when learning to write: "If you would make a man your friend, let him do you a favor."

Balboa shrugged. "You owe me nothing," he said.

Perez waved aside the remark. "There is something I can do for you," he said. "It may save your life a dozen times. Also your pretty face." The soldier rubbed his own gargoyle-like features and grinned.

"You mean the wrestling, as you practice it?"

"Correct. And best not look on it with scorn like a fob. All fighting is brutal. I'm the man who knows that, along with all the tricks. Are you interested, *compañero*?"

In the following three months there unfolded before Balboa all the tricks of the savage craft of brawling. He learned the blow which had paralyzed him: the almost nerveless edge of the hand connecting with the sensitive upper lip. Juan Perez showed him a wide variety of new holds and blows. He was taught the location of the nerve centers of the body and how to reach or protect them. Then there were the methods of disarming, gouging, kneeing and kicking.

Master and student were friends until Balboa was called before his captain and reprimanded. "Mind the company you keep!" he was told. "Remember you are a *hidalgo.*"

By that time Balboa had learned another thing from Juan Perez, a lesson which would one day make him the greatest of the Spanish *conquistadores.* He understood the thinking of the common soldier who forever after was his friend.

If there was little combat in the closing months of the war with the Moors, there was no lack of adventure. The desperate enemy tried every stratagem to get food.

A spy brought word near Christmas of 1491 that a large Moorish force had attacked another Christian caravan near Baza, far to the north. The raiders were expected to reach home that night with prisoners and plunder.

Balboa was among those chosen to intercept the Moors. Together with about a hundred others he donned armor and a heavy cloak before mounting his steed, for while it was mild on the plain, snow and ice could be expected up in the pass. The horsemen reached the place selected for ambush, which was ten miles from Granada, at sunset. Scouts were sent out and the terrain inspected. Overhead ragged clouds promised a dark night.

At midnight there were no signs of the returning Moors. Some declared this was a trap and that they themselves would be ambushed on their return by a powerful force from Granada. The captain remained firm. At two o'clock in the chill morning he and his aides rode through the ranks to inspect the foot soldiers.

Just before three o'clock in the morning riders dashed into camp with news. Fires had been lighted in the deserted Moorish signal towers to the north. Before another hour had passed the sky cleared and a waning moon cast a pallid light on the trail. Soon scouts brought word that a war party of several hundred white-clad Moors was approaching with many prisoners and much loot.

The soldier showed Balboa many new holds and blows

By laying their ears to the frozen ground the men could hear the rumble of faraway hoofs. A last inspection was made. The cavaliers mounted. Balboa was with a detachment of twenty riders who would be in the first wave of attack. They had orders to wait until almost half the Moorish advance guard had passed through the defile that opened into the valley.

Before dawn the outriders reached the pass. Now that they were close to home, they laughed and talked loudly, glad to be out of the snow-lashed mountains and back in an area of comparative warmth. In the moonlight Balboa saw the flash of curved scimitars and the glint of armor showing under turbans and flowing gowns. The enemy's horses were beautiful Arabians bedecked in embroidered, jewel-studded housings.

Balboa sat tense in a shadow as almost half the escort passed. The Spaniards' horses, trained to fight, were restless and broke out into snorts with their steamy breathing. The men held their lances ready. Then came the signal to attack.

"Santiago!"

Voices lifted to shout the battle cry. The Spanish cavaliers and the foot soldiers charged onto the trail, splitting the enemy ranks. As the dark-skinned warriors sounded their trumpets and shouted *la Alla ila Alla*—there is no God but God—Balboa said a hasty prayer to Santa Clara, patron saint of Moguer.

The Moors recovered quickly, for they were great night fighters. One of them, with face hidden, tried to unseat Balboa, whose horse wheeled and pawed, knocking the Moor to the snow. Amid the bedlam of shrieks, trumpets and shouts, Balboa felt the exhilaration of battle.

Another Moor sprang from behind a boulder, slashing upward with his scimitar. Balboa caught the blow on his buckler. Still another Moor then rode him down. He was thrust from his horse and landed heavily on the ice-crusted shale. A fourth man leaped upon him, dagger drawn. Sword still at his side, Balboa remembered his lessons from Juan Perez. He twisted to one side and launched a kick with both feet. The force of it sent the man flying backward.

Then Balboa was in the clear with his sword, master of all within range. Through fifteen minutes of fierce fighting he accounted for many of the sixty Moors who fell. Eyes alert, he also observed while he slashed and cut. There was a system in the manner in which the Spanish veterans cut off, disarmed and corralled the foe. All this the young *hidalgo* saw and fixed in his mind.

Most of the frightened captives were herded away under a waiting guard. The troops were disarmed, and any who fought back were slain. Before the last man had fallen the Spaniards were on the march lest they be surprised by reinforcements from Granada. They took with them choice Barbary horses, expensive armor, and gold and booty of many kinds. This was one of the last encounters before the fall of Granada.

Two days after the start of the New Year in 1492 the Moors surrendered. For the first time in eight hundred years Spain was free of the invader.

Balboa was in the great royal procession that advanced on the Alhambra amid the blare of trumpets. Ranks were swelled inside the Tower Gate of Justice by five hundred wretched men still in chains. These captive Spaniards blinked and sobbed. They could hardly believe that at last they were free of the dungeons where many had spent as long as twenty years.

Boabdil, the cruel "little king" of the Moors, was released by Their Majesties. He left in tears, upbraided by his mother who had guided him through middle age. To the Spaniards the disgrace of the Moor seemed sufficient punishment. The army then swarmed over the great city, awed by its strong ramparts, heavy fortifications and beautiful gardens. Food was hauled in for the starving thousands who had been reduced to eating boiled shoe leather amid the glistening golden mosques and richly furnished houses. Then began the dull mopping-up campaign.

Like others interested in arms Balboa viewed the future with little hope. Spain was at peace. What now were the prospects for fighting men?

The answer developed slowly but the gleam of an idea was formed there at the Alhambra. As the King and Queen gave audiences in the huge Gold Room of the Alhambra, the Age of Discovery was about to open. Before the monarchs came a strong-faced man whose hair had turned from red to white since the time Balboa had first seen him at the convent of La Rabida.

Christopher Columbus, the Genoese sea captain, had come again to renew his plea for ships with which to prove the world was round. And this time he was successful.

"There is the man who holds my future," Juan Perez told Balboa. "I, for one, want to believe him. He'll find this land of Cathay by going west. That means strong arms will be needed."

"Perhaps so," and Balboa nodded. There indeed

Christopher Columbus renewed his plea for ships

might be his solution, as well as a chance to gain both gold and honor.

"No 'perhaps' about it," Perez insisted. "Europe is worn out. We need new lands to conquer. Head that way when you can, lad."

The thought had grown stronger in Balboa's mind when he secured his release two months later. He shook hands for the last time with Juan Perez, still bound to service, and spurred for home. It was spring-time in Andalusia when his foam-flecked charger thundered through the city gates of Moguer.

3

The Ocean Sea

"No room for landsmen!"

That was the word spread from the plazas of Palos, Moguer and Huelva. Christopher Columbus found it difficult to get anyone who would voyage into the Sea of Darkness, yet he wanted to ship only mariners.

"It is true," Francisco Nino told Balboa. Now nineteen, Nino had signed on as "gromet," or ship's boy. "The voyage is for discovery alone, *amigo*.

There will be no men-at-arms. Perhaps later, when we have discovered Cathay."

"I would do anything," Balboa declared.

"So would many. Yet consider this: I have served my time at sea but I must ship as gromet." Nino made a face. "At that I am lucky. I do not fool myself. I go at all only because my brother Juan owns the *Nina*. The same with my second brother, Peralonso. He sails as chief pilot in the flagship *Santa Maria*."

And so it was. Despite his offers, Balboa was one of those who remained behind when the three ships of the armada weighed anchor at dawn on August 3, 1492.

The little ships were in sight all day and Balboa went with the crowd to watch from the promontory at the convent of La Rabida. If his heart was heavy with disappointment he could see another in even greater distress. Twelve-year-old Diego Columbus wept as his father sailed away.

When the Admiral returned in the spring of the next year all Spain was afire. The world was round! There was a sea route to the Indies! People from distant cities thronged Moguer to watch the discoverers enter the Cathedral. The stories of the mariners were fantastic but they were backed by proof—

painted savages, dragon-like lizards, talking parrots, and gold! Men who had held back because of fear now fought to make the second voyage. But only those with the strongest influence found places in the fleet.

Balboa was not one of these fortunates nor did he find a place on the third voyage. He hung about the docks, he mingled with the native captives, and he wrote many letters of application. While he made a precarious living with his sword he sought the company of sailors. From them he heard that ships were sailing illegally from Sanlucar de Barrameda, so there he rode.

Sanlucar was the refuge of criminals, political fugitives and adventurers. Balboa wandered down to the waterfront, a maze of shacks where cutthroats and robbers lurked. This lawless element found the pickings good near the docks, for many people were to be found there, their personal belongings piled high around them, seeking ships to bear them to safety. These were the Jews, all of whom Queen Isabella had exiled from Spain.

But none at the rough seaport would have Balboa. "Lad," a shipmaster whispered in a waterfront tavern, "Spain could use men like you, but I can't stow you away. Why? You're too outstanding. That sword!

Your looks!" He glanced up at Balboa, now twenty-one, and nodded approval at the handsome, blond-bearded face, the look of determination, and the clean strength of the young man.

"Their Majesties know nothing of these secret voyages," the mariner explained. "Recollect: when permission is given to sail, the Crown claims one-fifth of all gold and pearls we bring back. Besides, others have to be buttered. Suppose word ever got out that I commanded on any secret voyage? Well, sir, I would lose my ship, all I brought back and—my head."

Balboa still hoped for a place on some ship. He dared not venture to the new campaign in Italy, or travel to the French court, lest he miss his chance. He earned scarcely enough to satisfy his great appetite by teaching the art of the sword to boys and by offering his services as a guard to wealthy travelers. He tried to stay close to Moguer.

Meanwhile, Fray Juan was corresponding in his behalf with friends in Seville. "Be patient, my son," the old priest advised. "I well know it is a cross at your age. But you will one day reach the Indies. Remember my words, that God is saving you for a great destiny."

Eight years after the first voyage of Columbus, Peralonso Nino returned from some newly discovered land with fifty pounds of declared pearls. It was said that he had smuggled as many more. When the news spread, interest in the New World was rekindled and at last Balboa was given his chance to sail across the Ocean Sea.

Rodrigo de Bastidas, a wealthy notary of Seville, had been granted a Crown charter to seek treasure on the Pearl Coast of Tierra Firme (the northern shore of South America). He was fitting out two ships which were to be commanded and manned by the best available talent in Spain. Fray Juan's connections assured Balboa a billet as *escudero,* one of a dozen fighting men.

Eager and full of thanks, Balboa joined the expedition at Cadiz in March of 1501 to have his first look at the ships. The *Santa Maria de Gracia* lay alongside the stone dock with her consort, the little caravel *San Anton.* The flagship was about sixty tons burthen and some seventy feet in length. She had been newly painted a brilliant yellow and trimmed black at the wales. Men were still gilding the figurehead and stern lantern. Masts had been scraped and gleamed with oil; fresh tar shone on the standing rigging. Sails furled on the yards were yellowish in color.

"Stand clear! Stand clear!"

Oxcarts rumbled along the quay and dumped sacks and casks alongside the ships. Drivers lashed the animals and shouted rude warnings at dock-side loafers. On lines rigged from the cocked main yard, men slung the precious cargo aboard. Supercargoes bawled orders below. The ships were taking on supplies as well as trade goods for a year-long voyage. The ragtag of the port gathered to watch the lading for this was a treasure voyage.

On sailing day the crowding was at its height. Over the gangway came visitors, King's officers, and the seamen's wives who in those days made the voyage, berthing forward with their husbands. Last-minute consignments and armor were dumped on deck and shoved clear of the bulwarks. Fresh fruit and vegetables were tossed in the yawl on the main hatch. At noon the order came to cast off.

"You *gentlemen!*" The bosun herded Balboa and the other *hidalgos* aft. "Out of the way before one of you gets hung in the bight of a line."

Huge ash oars were shoved through the side ports. Hairy, tattooed seamen wearing red stocking caps manned the sweeps. The ships swung away from the

Over the gangway came visitors and King's officers

cheering dock and out into the crowded bay, picking their way through a glut of shipping. Barefooted seamen, the older ones bowlegged from the rolling of ships, ran aloft to cast off gaskets. The vessels cleared the roadstead and a cold wind blew down from the north, making the long masthead pennants stream far out to leeward.

Orders were bawled from the sterncastle. Sails were dropped and sheeted; yards were hoisted. As the bulges of canvas filled with loud reports the ship heeled. Soon water bubbled under her bows.

Bravely the two ships stood out past the fortress of Santa Catalina and exchanged salutes. The already homesick gromets hid tears and wistfully viewed the fading shore. But for Balboa the departure meant the end of frustrating years. At last he was outward bound for the Indies. He sighted ahead eagerly.

"All hands! All hands!"

The shrill pipe of the bosun's whistle called the ship's company aft for the time-honored ceremony of setting sea watches. A gromet's high voice called out the half hour as he capsized the sand glass, the only timepiece aboard. The pilot had taken a bearing over the compass. Now he shouted down to the helmsman below: "West and by south!" They were off soundings now, clear of the land and bound for the Canary Islands seven hundred miles away.

"Men!" Stern, square-bearded Captain Juan de la Cosa frowned down into the waist of the ship, ignoring the females. "You know our destination," he said. "You know your duties." The skipper then outlined the duties, warned against fighting, loafing, and stealing from shipmates, and walked to leeward. A horny fist thumped the mahogany rail. "Let every man obey my orders. Let one fail and that man will think he shipped with Satan. That's all!"

Sailors were assigned to the starboard and larboard (or port) watches to begin earning their twelve *maravedies* per day—about thirty cents.

When the hands had been dismissed Balboa and his comrades-in-arms were called aside for a short lecture by the Captain. He ended with the advice: "If we should founder, no one is to take his armor—unless he wishes to be well anchored in one thousand fathoms. A pleasant voyage, gentlemen."

The ship began to labor as the quartering wind hauled forward and freshened to kick up a beam sea. The first to get seasick sought the lee rail while old salts jeered them in their misery. Decks were sloshed down with icy sea water to clear away the filth of the port. As the sun set a fire blazed in the stone hearth forward and the women squabbled over the evening meal.

A week of squally weather followed the departure. Then the lookouts picked up the high peak of Tenerife twenty-four hours before they sighted land. To Balboa the week spent at the Canary Islands taking on wood, water, fresh meat and cheeses was time wasted. Even though he had grown used to his small quarters, the scant food and constant motion, nothing mattered but to get to the Indies. He for one was glad when the order came to weigh anchor.

The ships now ran before the northeast trades, the deep blue, white-crested seas following them and the sky overhead spotted with clean, billowy clouds. Balboa and the others spent their time in the lee of the bulwarks or in the shadow cast by the great mainsail. Europe—with its walled cities, narrow, crooked streets, smoky public rooms and castles of damp stone—seemed farther in the distance than could be measured by miles. Here was the freedom of the sea.

And always there were yarns: stories about voyages said to have been made westward as far as Japan in the time of King Solomon; tales about the phantom islands of Saint X, Encorporada and La Catolique where gold grew on rocks. The older seamen told of ocean monsters, living pearls, ghost ships, mermaids and cities below the sea. As always, most of these were lies. But Balboa learned that the mariners possessed far more knowledge than scholars ashore.

Veterans of the Ocean Sea, as the Atlantic was called, knew that Columbus had not reached the Orient. Beyond the chain of islands already discovered lay a vast mainland. On the famous *mappemonde* then being drawn by their Captain this was shown as an unbroken coastline from Brazil up to Labrador. What we know today as the Pacific was thought to be solid land.

To Balboa geography was less interesting than treasure. Only after years of sailing could a man become a pilot or captain, skilled in the use of such instruments as the quadrant, cross staff and astrolabe. So Balboa paid more attention to lectures on pearls, and how to recognize gold-bearing rock, than to explanations of navigation.

"All I have told you," said Captain Cosa after a talk with Balboa, "has passed quickly through your ears. But you will attend to this: late tomorrow—our twenty-sixth day at sea—we should raise land."

Shore birds appeared in the morning. By late afternoon bits of twigs and leaves were seen overside. Surface fish splashed and sleeping turtles spotted the calm, slow-rolling ocean.

"Tierra! Tierra!"

As predicted, lookouts gave the welcome hail just before sunset. Next day the mariners skirted a bold island covered with vegetation and christened it Green Isle. (One day men would call this Barbados, one of the string of islands that fringes the outer Caribbean.)

The ships stood almost due west, heading for Tierra Firme. At last they made a landfall on the northern shore of South America and skirted long, white beaches. The ships were anchored at night and sailors took soundings constantly when under way, for this was known to be a treacherous coast. When they hauled abeam of the last cape recognized by Captain Cosa on his voyage with Hojeda the ships were hove-to.

All hands were again mustered, for they were about to pioneer. Rodrigo de Bastidas then took command. The meek notary of Seville became an aggressive, treasure-hungry hunter. His voice cracked with authority.

"We are here for wealth," he told the men. "First we will try kindness on these savages." The notary scowled. "Any man who puts an Indian to the sword without my consent goes to the main yardarm with a noose around his neck. Understand me!"

There began four months of exploring, searching and trading along two hundred miles of strange coastline. Only Balboa and the other fighting men were allowed to venture inland and then just for short distances. The natives were men of short stature with heavy arms and huge chests, and they looked quite fierce with their ringed noses and bodies streaked red by smears of dye made from the pulp of a native plant. It was known they used a poison on their arrow tips which caused certain death.

At first most of the Indians were friendly. A proclamation was read, inviting them to become Christians, and they were willing enough to exchange shields, rings and gold nuggets for colored glass beads and hawk's bells. Some even stripped off gold ceremonial ornaments for the sailors' red woolen caps. The Spaniards were shown pearl beds but found few perfect specimens.

As the ships neared the Gulf of Uraba, where Colombia and Panama now join, Bastidas became greedy. He already had three iron chests loaded with pearls, ornaments and seventy-five pounds of pure gold. His assets were almost five million *maravedíes*. But that

Lookouts sighted land just before sunset

was not enough. He seized a large group of Indians and had them chained and thrown into the hold. He also stole considerable dye wood. Slaves and cargo would bring a nice profit.

"It is the end of our trading on this coast," Captain Cosa predicted.

And that was true. The Spaniards were unable to land again and so crossed the gulf to Darien (or Panama, as it is known today). Balboa stepped ashore, little knowing that he would one day make history at this spot. What he saw and later remembered was a coastal tribe of friendly people who used no poison and were open-handed with their few supplies. The Spaniards suspected the natives of hiding their treasures but had no chance to investigate, for an emergency put an end to Bastidas' exploration and plundering.

The *Santa Maria* and *San Anton* were sinking! For three weeks men had been laboring longer each day at the wooden pumps. Now they could no longer make them work. When the ships were beached and careened the sailors could hardly believe what they saw. After less than half a year the wood on the bottoms looked old and rotted. The broma (or sea worm) of these slimy tropical waters had riddled every plank from keel to waterline.

"We will sail for home!" Bastidas declared. "Five weeks at most. We cannot afford to fail!"

Captain Cosa shook his head. It would not be as easy as the outward-bound passage. He himself had sailed homeward with Columbus at this very time of year, in late November, and he remembered how rough the voyage had been. They would have to stand far north, then catch the fresh westerlies which would soon work every plank loose. "First we must overhaul these bottoms," he said.

The Crown contract did not permit Bastidas to call at Hispaniola, Spanish headquarters in the New World, so a course was set for Jamaica. Men were at the pumps day and night. The skipper paced the poop at night or dozed in a wicker chair. Everyone watched the weather, for even a moderate blow meant foundering. Water rose in the hold to spoil the food and the women's tempers flared. From below came the wail of frightened captives.

Balboa saw the mainland sink slowly below the horizon. Was this to be the end of his adventure? Either to be drowned at sea or, by some miracle, reach Spain and be paid off with a few pesos? He had seen a sample of the Indies' wealth and he had observed the short-sighted policy of the greedy Bastidas. If he were in command, he reflected, he would know how to conduct an expedition—even though he was only twenty-five. The Indians must be treated firmly, but with some kindness. Then a strong force should march inland to the mountains. But it was idle to dream. He was just another *hidalgo!*

The ships labored up to Jamaica and were hove down for major repairs. Bottoms were caulked with fiber and pitched; new planking replaced the more hopeless sections. A spare sail was passed under the bottom of the *Santa Maria* and secured on deck to "fother" an especially bad leak. After a month the Spaniards started for home but bad weather forced them into the lee of Boatswain's Island, near the coast of Hispaniola. Here the time dragged until late in February when Bastidas could stand the delay no longer.

"This is foolhardy," Captain Cosa warned as they headed into the Gulf of Gonave.

By mid-afternoon the ships were in trouble. Black clouds piled up on the horizon ahead and the wind began to box the compass. At sunset it blew strongly out of the southeast and Captain Cosa was forced to run down on the lofty shore of Hispaniola. This time there was no chance of picking shelter.

At one o'clock in the morning the *Santa Maria* had only two feet of freeboard. Sail was reduced, and lan-

tern signals were exchanged with the *San Anton*.
Men and women huddled in the lee of the aftercastle
as rain came with the wind and rising sea. Flashes of
lightning showed a ragged shore to starboard. The
pleas of the chained Indians became hysterical.

The heavy chests were pulled out and hefted into
the yawl by Balboa and his strong companions. Bastidas joined the officers in driving the men as the
boat was hauled to larboard and made ready for
launching.

A curved stretch of sand showed dead ahead when
lightning streaked across the black sky. Captain Cosa
shouted down orders to the helmsman to ratch off
and make for the beach.

But at that moment a great swell lifted the *Santa
Maria* and sent her scudding toward a reef of jagged
rocks. The *San Anton* had already grounded. The
Santa Maria dropped, then lifted again and rolled far
over. Next time, with helm hard over, she came down
hard on the reef and was hulled forward and amidships. The screams from below suddenly ceased.

Only superb seamanship got the heavily laden
yawl launched and clear of the wreckage. All except
the Indians reached shore under the roll of thunder
and the lash of rain.

It was the night of February 28, 1502, when Balboa waded ashore. He was soaked, without money, and thousands of miles from home. Yet as he gripped his sword he felt strangely full of hope.

4

Young Conquistadores

By daybreak the storm had blown itself out. Half a hundred men and their women watched the *Santa Maria de Gracia* and her worm-eaten consort shuffle below the beautiful turquoise water. The castaways exchanged uneasy glances as the triangular fins of sharks cut the surface above the wrecks. All hands were hungry, wet and exhausted. They scuffed the coral sand near what is now the great Caribbean city of Port-au-Prince, Haiti. The settlement at Santo Domingo (known today as Ciudad Trujillo) lay two hundred miles away.

"This ends our expedition," said Bastidas, who assured the people they would all be paid as soon as possible. "But first it is our sacred duty to reach Santo Domingo with our treasure. We will separate into three parties, for we must live off the land."

All extra arms were destroyed and the scant provisions divided. The fighting men were split up, Balboa and three others going with Juan de la Cosa who chose to follow the coast where a seaman could at least get a bearing.

Half starved, stalked all the way by lurking savages, the party of fifteen men pushed on along the rough southern shore of Hispaniola. At night they heard the eerie cries of ocelots up in the hills; by day the sun burned down on them. Swarms of insects raised welts on their sweating bodies. Their cheers were feeble when they came in sight of the town after two weeks of marching.

Santo Domingo in 1502 was a frontier settlement of dirty huts and crowded wooden shanties built on the right bank of the Ozama River. Along the trails that passed for streets miserable Taino Indians cowered, many of them with their noses and ears cropped. Soldiers of the governor swaggered and bullied. It was a detachment of these fellows who first greeted the castaways.

Without explanation the entire Bastidas party was

shoved into jail and there it remained for more than
a month. Release came only when the new governor
arrived.

Don Nidolas de Ovando arrived in April with
2,500 colonists, men-at-arms and mariners in a fleet
of thirty sail. The new Governor waited on the wealthy
Bastidas promptly. The other men were released and
promised audiences soon. But it was another month
before Balboa was granted an interview.

"Another young cavalier," said Ovando with scorn
as he faced the ragged, hungry swordsman. "Come
to gamble and quarrel and wait for gold to fall in
your lap. Faugh! Who lets you people come out
here?"

"My sword is at the disposal of His Majesty," Balboa replied angrily. "I seek employment on the mainland, to the west. I am no wastrel."

The Governor hid his uneasiness. He called for a
clerk. "Very well, sir swordsman," he snapped. "To
the west you shall go. Here!"

When he studied the written orders outside Balboa was less surprised than disappointed. He was
being shipped west, true enough—to the western end
of Hispaniola, one hundred miles beyond where he
had been wrecked. The orders gave him a thirty-acre
grant of land and twenty Indians. His directions were
to raise pigs and grow crops. All the world might be

The swordsman was left to raise pigs and grow crops

afire to conquer new lands and discover gold, but he—as good a fighting man as any in the Kingdom—was to be a farmer!

Salvatierra de la Sabana was the name of the new settlement on the southwestern peninsula of Hispaniola, three hundred miles from the capital. Balboa's farmhouse was built under palm trees near a little beach of white and perfect sand. The soil around looked rich even to the non-rural eye of the swordsman. No doubt it would produce fine crops of maize, pepper and cassava for the officials who arrived in Santo Domingo to govern the island. Balboa looked at a squealing young pig which had followed him into the house. He vowed he would not remain.

His sword and armor were well oiled and taken better care of than the farm tools. He organized his twenty Indians and set them an example as he worked at their side in building shelters and tilling the fields. Alone at night, pacing the beach, his dreams were of conquest and he longed for action. He was ready for any adventure that summer when a rider reined up and shouted his name. It was a courier from Captain Juan Ponce de Leon, who had been with Columbus on his second voyage.

"The Captain remembers your sword at Granada," the messenger said. "He begs you to join him at Higuey. The Governor has declared war on the natives who refuse to work in the mines. You are offered the commission of lieutenant."

For the next two years Balboa did not see his farm and he was ruthlessly cheated. As for the campaign, it was a disgrace for Spanish soldiers, then considered the best in the world. The Taino Indians were not fierce fighters and they had no more gold to give, yet they were killed anyway. Despite their fine leadership, even hardened Spanish veterans felt disgust at the slaughter.

With other officers Balboa hung his head in shame at the plaza of Santo Domingo when Queen Anacaona, widow of Chief Caonabo, was burned alive at the stake.

"Take heart, young man!" Captain Ponce de Leon slapped Balboa on the back. "Conquest is always cruel. Remember, we are soldiers. Now come along, I want to reward your service to me."

The Captain led the way to his house in the new town that had been built on the left bank of the Ozama after the old settlement was destroyed by a great hurricane. Balboa was shown out to a small kennel. Here he saw a huge, battle-scarred Spanish mastiff and with him a younger dog—a yellowish, muscular animal with a black muzzle.

"This is Becerillo," Ponce de Leon said, pointing to

the big animal. "You have seen him in battle. And this is his son. You can have the little fellow if you will."

"You are too generous," Balboa protested, patting the dog.

"Not a bit. They are father and son. Soon they will be fighting. I expect you will need this fellow."

"Thank you. But I must have the naming of him," Balboa said.

"Fair enough."

"He will be Leoncico—the little lion. Do you mind, Captain?"

Ponce de Leon laughed. "Not at all." Then, "Step down with me to the Marina," he said. "I want you to meet some other young blades I am watching."

As they came on the waterfront of the Ozama Balboa looked with interest at the ships. More arrived every month from Spain. He heard that two captains—Alonso de Hojeda and Diego de Nicuesa—had been given a joint license to explore and conquer Darien, the very land he had seen with Bastidas.

Balboa followed Ponce de Leon into a low-doored tavern, and then to a back room. Here for the first time he met Hernan Cortes and Francisco Pizarro. With them was Bartolome Hurtado, the young explorer who would be Balboa's friend for the next ten years.

Cortes and Pizarro were cousins but it would have been hard to find two more dissimilar men. Cortes, swordsman and scholar, had attended the University of Salamanca until his quarreling made it wise for him to seek his fortune in the New World. He was a smooth-talking, friendly man, then in his twenties and already dreaming of conquest.

Pizarro, beetle-browed, dark-skinned and as big as Balboa, could neither read nor write. He had been a swineherd in Estremadura and had run away, first to the Italian campaign, then to Hispaniola. Now in his early thirties, he was shrewd and showed a surly manner.

"Show my comrade-in-arms the map," said Ponce de Leon, addressing the three men. "I must be off. And you, Balboa, pick up Leoncico when you wish."

Hurtado, round-faced and sturdy, brought out a rough parchment and borrowed Balboa's sword to hold down one edge. The chart showed the coastline from Yucatan, past Darien, to the northern part of South America. Bays and river mouths were well defined and even trails inland were shown.

"No doctors in Europe have anything so complete as this," Cortes said. "Only second-hand exploring can be done in the universities. That is why a few men like ourselves can shape the future history of Spain."

"We are not the only ones here," Pizarro grumbled.

"No?" Cortes raised his eyebrows. "Look around, Cousin. The city is choked with people, true. But how many can lead and fight? Most are here to get their money at second hand. A few—a very few, Pizarro—will go out first to conquer."

Balboa frowned and ran a hand through his beard. Ponce de Leon must believe him to be one of those few. He thought of old Fray Juan while Cortes told his dream of conquering the Aztec empire. De Leon was going north, he heard. Pizarro was sailing south with Hojeda.

"And you, Balboa?" Cortes asked. "Surely from what I hear of your sword you are not content to run that hotel for pigs?"

"Not content by a long sea league," Balboa said with a sad smile. "But bound to it none the less. After the campaign I learned that the law forbids a man in debt to leave Hispaniola. And I am much in debt."

"Who holds your paper?"

"His name is Martin Fernandez de Encisco. A lawyer, I hear."

"*Santissima!*" Cortes pounded the table. "A lawyer he is—a *bachiller*. More than that: a dragon is a lamb compared with Encisco. I am sorry for you, *compañero*. You had best pitch camp at the graveyard and wait."

Balboa rode back to the farm with Leoncico, the sole reward for his service in the Higuey campaign. Like his father, he was in the clutches of the law. What he had learned of Indian fighting, his experience against the Moor, his hundreds of sword engagements—these should give him a value. But no! He must grow old a farmer.

The farm at Salvatierra had run down badly in two years. To keep himself occupied, Balboa put all his energy into reviving the place. From sunrise until after dark he could be seen in the fields digging or at work with hammer and nails. He spared the whip and nursed the sick, showing more concern for the natives than any of the other Spanish farmers. He was a great favorite with the people, especially the young men. Never had they seen a man of such strength and such good humor as this blond giant from across the Ocean Sea. If only the others were like him!

In a short time the farm began to prosper. Balboa laboriously figured out how long it would take him to work clear of debt and felt encouraged. But he had not reckoned with the shrewd swindlers from the city. His simple mistakes in arithmetic were turned into a profit by Encisco. Balboa suspected nothing. He did not think to cheat so it never occurred to him that others might cheat him. He was more interested in news of discovery and the gossip of Santo Domingo than in prices.

As time passed he grew restless and each piece of news made him that much more anxious to leave the farm. Rodrigo de Bastidas had returned to Santo Domingo a rich man and was engaged in trade. Diego Columbus was the new Governor. Ponce de Leon had left for Puerto Rico. When Balboa heard that even Francisco Pizarro was leaving for the south he decided to visit Santo Domingo. He loaded swine and foodstuffs aboard a boat he had built in his spare time, a beamy craft that looked like the river boats on the Tinto. His plan was to sell his livestock and supplies to meet expenses while he was hunting a sponsor. Surely someone would have faith in him!

But none would help Balboa in the bustling city. Bastidas pretended not to remember him. Juan de la Cosa was not rich. Diego Columbus was building a mansion and, besides, did not want to offend Encisco.

Balboa sought out Cortes. He did so only for company's sake because, like himself, the future *conquistador* was always without funds. Balboa found him in the back room of a tavern with Hurtado. They were speaking of a knife fight when Balboa entered. It appeared that Cortes had been forced to discipline one Andrés de Garabito. Greetings had barely been ex-

"I will not hear any talk of your sailing!"

changed when a tavern boy banged on the door and entered.

"Captains," said the boy in a warning voice, *"Bachiller* Encisco comes this way. Do you wish . . ."

"Ha!" The lawyer pushed in, ferret eyes darting about, then settling on Balboa. He was a thin, rat-faced man with a manner that was at once snappish and cringing.

"So!" Encisco continued to glare at Balboa. "You talk of borrowing money, eh? Of getting out of my debt? And here you swill with these other 'boy conquerors.' Woe betide those who roister while others sweat."

Cortes laughed without humor. "Stop sweating, *bachiller,*" he said as he placed a restraining hand on Balboa's arm. "What do you want?"

Encisco leveled a bony finger at Balboa. "This scamp came into town with supplies. They belong to me. I won't have them sold to another. I have two ships in the stream due to sail next week under my command." Encisco paused for breath, then glowered at Hurtado. "You know that," he snapped. "You are sailing with me."

"Bachiller," said Balboa, "I have a suggestion . . ."

"No, no, no!" Encisco squeaked. "I will not hear any talk of your sailing. And don't think of stowing away. I will have those ships watched and searched. The law . . ."

"What do you want?" Balboa felt his temper rising.

"Better," said Encisco. "Much better." He drew a legal document from his belt pouch. "I have here a list of your supplies. My men checked the warehouse. If you will sign . . ." He cut off his words and avoided the hard stares of the three young men.

Balboa scanned the manifest and was about to hand it back when a certain item caught his eye and gave him a brilliant idea. His anger abated. He hid a smile and pretended to study the list. He knew now how he would leave Hispaniola!

5

The Stowaway

On a sultry morning in September, 1510, the waterfront of Santo Domingo bustled with loading activity.
Crowds gathered early to await the departure of Encisco's flagship and a small corvette named the *Chapinera*. Lighters hurried deck cargo out to the ships
anchored in the Ozama. This final lading included a
barrel marked *Supplies for the Voyage—Flour*. In
the barrel crouched Balboa and Leoncico, a wrapped
sword wedged between them.

Balboa had been nailed in at the warehouse by Hurtado and slung aboard the crowded ship while sharp-eyed guards kept a lookout for stowaways. When the big barrel thudded onto the main deck it had been hauled forward and to starboard.

"None suspect, *compañero*." Hurtado spoke above a chink in the barrel as he gazed shoreward. "But keep that dog quiet when we salute the Fort."

Bells chimed at the Chapel of the Rosary on the east bank of the Ozama. Visitors climbed over the side as final calls of farewell drifted across the flat water. Seamen shifted the barrel once for a searching party. Balboa held his breath. The minutes seemed to drag until the order came to get underway.

Oars were shipped for the row down to the open sea. Voices from aloft told the perspiring stowaway that gaskets were being cast off, sails made ready to be dropped. At the windlass the men sang a hoarse chanty. Finally Balboa heard the shout:

"Anchor's aweigh!"

The milling of one hundred and fifty men-at-arms and the crisp orders from the poop drowned out the cheers from shore. Bells continued to peal, for this was a most important sailing. Encisco must relieve the struggling settlement at San Sebastian, Spain's only settlement on the mainland. (This was located on the coast of what is known as Colombia today.)

Balboa shifted cautiously in the steaming barrel and patted Leoncico. How well he remembered the lush, green shores which he had first seen from the deck of Bastidas' ship. He wondered if the coastal Indians had become friendly.

His reflections were abruptly interrupted by the discharge of the light cannon. Balboa placed a hand on the back of his trembling dog as the ship's salute was answered by the guns of Fort Saint Joseph.

Now all hands were making sail. Canvas dropped out of the gear and was sheeted home. Everyone on deck grabbed the main halyard. Pulling together, they slowly raised the great spar from which the main-sail was set. The course filled with a sharp crack. The barrel rocked when the ship heeled. Other sails filled. Then came the gentle motion of a ship under sail.

"No sound now, *compañero*." Hurtado hissed the words close to the barrel. "A final search is being made. You are almost safe."

Man and dog tensed. The searching party was checking off the men-at-arms. The main hatch was being inspected, the sail locker overhauled. Close by a voice suggested examining the cargo on deck. Balboa wiped sweat from his face. If he remained undetected that would be a sign of God's judgment. He thought of Fray Juan's words about his destiny.

Again the action of the ship cut in on his reflections. An order was shouted to the men at the braces; the mainsail was being backed. The ship was heaving-to so that the official party could be put overside into an escort vessel.

Then the ship was underway again, heeling more sharply before a fresh breeze that drove her over the long ground swell. Very slowly Balboa began to unwrap his sword. He smiled grimly in the darkness. He tried to visualize the scene to come. There was still great risk, he knew, but there was also much humor in the situation.

Encisco, the *bachiller,* was as greedy as a vulture. This being his first command, he would be nervous as well. His duty was merely to deliver supplies but it was common knowledge that he had other ambitions. His money was invested in the enterprise. Some said he hoped to replace Hojeda. The lawyer fancied himself as a *conquistador.*

"Get ready, Balboa!" Hurtado spoke rapidly. "But give me time to mingle with the others before you cry out. His Ridiculousness is about to call a muster."

Balboa braced himself. He waited for the gromet

to finish the singsong that followed the turning of the half-hour glass. Then he nudged Leoncico. Man and dog began a weird outcry, accompanied by the heavy banging of the sword hilt.

"*Caramba!*"

Soldiers ran to the barrel. What manner of cargo did this ship carry? What kind of flour could knock, bark and bawl out in so commanding a tone?

The barrel was quickly broached. Balboa hiked out, Leoncico leaping after him. Together they pushed past the curious crowd. Balboa brushed himself as he walked aft to the quarterdeck. He ran lightly up the ladder and stepped to windward where he planted his sword blade in the hard deck. With Leoncico growling at his side, he stood there and smiled.

"You?" Encisco finally found his voice.

Balboa nodded as though to confirm the fact. He breathed deeply and sighted astern. The ragged surf-line of Hispaniola lay below the horizon. Only the steep, green slopes of the island loomed in the clear blue sky. The Governor's lugger was already hull down.

"What is this?" Encisco shrilled. "Who put you aboard, you . . . you criminal?" He shook a small fist and glared past Balboa into the faces of the grinning soldiers. But he jumped back when Leoncico began to rise.

"Master-at-Arms!" Encisco suddenly shouted. "Seize this fellow, Master-at-Arms," he ordered. "Into irons with him!"

The Master-at-Arms paused and eyed Balboa. He shrugged uncertainly. The entire ship's company crowded aft to the break of the poop. Youngsters climbed into the rigging for a better view.

"Hold!" Balboa placed his right hand on the sword hilt. "Calm yourself, *bachiller*," he advised in a firm voice. "Try to accept the fact that I am here."

"You pauper!" Encisco exploded. "Like father, like son. You embezzler. Do you know the law? Do you know the penalty for a stowaway?"

Balboa glanced up at the topmasts swaying against the cobalt sky. "Forget your law," he said. "I am aboard, and my armor is amidships there forward of the longboat—in that box marked bacon."

"Lay hold of him! Any of you!" Encisco's face was flushed; his thin lips quivered. "I order you men to seize him according to law." Encisco glared below where three soldiers laughed. They had broken open the case of "bacon" to reveal shining armor.

"Marooned!" Encisco spat out this sudden inspiration. "Yes, sir! That is the treatment. That is the prescribed punishment." He jumped about like a flea on a hot stove. He seemed to have forgotten that the stowaway was not yet in irons.

"Pilot! Navigator! I want distance and course to the nearest island. But wait!" A new idea had come to the lawyer. "That is too good for this rascal. First we heave-to. I'll have him keelhauled. Exactly! Keelhauled, then what's left of him goes onto a cannibal island." Encisco stepped forward, panting. "Those Caribs will feed well on him. And the law permits it."

Balboa had been watching the expressions of the men. Marooning meant nothing to them. But not a few would like the diversion of a bloody keelhauling. It was time to act. He drew his blade out of the deck and the well-trained Leoncico tensed, ready to go to work.

"The first man to move gets my steel," said Balboa, red with anger, his voice low and menacing. "Now attend to me, every man aboard. I am not another stowaway. No! *God has reserved me for great matters!* I do not say so to brag. I was told this by a priest."

Balboa turned to Encisco. "And you listen well to this, *bachiller*. Threaten me again—just once more—

and I'll run you through." The swordsman looked over the afterguard, then down at the rough company of hardened recruits. His green-blue eyes dared any man to move.

"Very well." There had not been the slightest movement from anybody, and the sword point returned to the deck with a violent jab that sank it a full three inches. Balboa leaned slightly over the hilt. *"Bachiller,"* he said in a commanding tone, "you will hold your wagging legal tongue while I tell you what will happen. There will be no keelhauling. There will be no marooning. Consider yourself lucky. You command the best sword arm in the New World. You have the services of my Leoncico. For the present, pay me what you wish—whatever a man-at-arms is worth. What do you say?"

"I say no!" Encisco's manner had become cautious. Astern, the lugger was out of sight. He hid his fear with argument. "Do you take me for a fool?" he asked craftily. "Do you imagine I fail to see your clumsy trap? If I condone your act perhaps I will be legally responsible for your debts. I say 'no' again."

"That is too bad." Balboa looked down at the men, then back at the fidgety *bachiller*. "I have another value," he said persuasively. "Perhaps you have not considered: I am the only man aboard who has sailed

"The first man to move gets my steel," warned Balboa

in the waters off San Sebastian. I know the land. I may be worth far more to every man aboard than any debt."

For a moment there was silence. The hum of the wind sounded loud in the rigging. Encisco looked uncertainly at the menacing blond figure, then down at the dog who seemed to read his thoughts.

While Encisco hesitated, not knowing what to say, Balboa's eyes swept the crowd. "What do you say, men?" he shouted.

When a cheer burst from the soldiers and crew Encisco mumbled something no one heard and stomped below.

Five days out of Santo Domingo the lookout at the main top picked up the hazy coast of Cartagena. Three hours later he sighted a lugger halfway to shore.

Forty men were crouched in the battered craft which had a scant six inches of freeboard. A tatter of sail gave them steerageway. Even at a distance it could be seen that the men were too weak to row. The corvette, sailing up ahead of the flagship, took the men off and left the battered lugger to her fate.

First to be helped aboard was Francisco Pizarro. His cheeks were gaunt under a matted black beard;

his dark skin showed blisters. Through swollen lips he mumbled what had happened.

The settlement at San Sebastian had been wiped out by Indians. Many had died; the wooden fort and the thirty huts had been burned to the ground. Spain no longer maintained an establishment on Tierra Firme. "Best turn back," Pizarro advised.

"Ridiculous!" Encisco's little eyes gleamed. "If Captain Hojeda has abandoned the settlement, then I am in nominal command. Possibly in legal possession." Head down, lips smirking, Encisco paced the deck and rubbed his bony hands.

Before heading westward the ships were brought close in to shore and anchored for the night. The following morning Encisco led a party ashore. He was accompanied by a scribe and a gold assayer but he did not include Balboa in the party. His hunger for loot made him unmindful of a possible ambush.

The boat party waited on the beach until almost nightfall. At last Encisco and his men returned— without gold. Scornful silence was the only form of greeting they received.

The two ships again made sail and skirted the coast, heading west and southwest for the pocket of water first visited by the Bastidas expedition. They were closing with a dangerous lee shore. Balboa recognized Caribana Point and, up ahead, Cape Goleta; he recalled that Juan de la Cosa had given the east shore a wide berth. He walked aft to sound a warning.

"Quiet!" Encisco rasped. "I command this ship."

"You stand to lose the ship," Balboa insisted. He pointed off to port at the marshy shore below the foothills of Uraba. "An undertow sets close to the headland," he continued. "When you round the point too close there are said to be baffling winds and a strong eddy."

"Get forward where you belong!"

Slowly the flagship ghosted in. To the north, off starboard, majestic mountains rose like a huge barrier. As though fearful of them Encisco set his course close in to Caribana. He ignored the pilot. Again Balboa came aft but this time he was too late even for a reprimand.

"Breakers ahead!"

The instant the lookout shouted, the ship seemed to have been gripped by a great invisible hand. The eddy caught her. The wind died. The helm went dead.

"Out oars!"

The command was never obeyed. The ship reeled in the clutch of the undertow. She dragged steadily

and swiftly toward a circle where breakers crashed on
black, porous rock. The astonished men felt fear as
the unseen force took over. The vessel yawed, then
saw-toothed crags crushed her sides. The main hatch
split open; cargo spewed out on gushers of sea water.
The bulwarks folded and men were toppled. Then
the ship was hurled by a tremendous surge into a
pocket of deep water and began to settle fast. Overhead the sun was shining brightly and offshore only
ripples creased the calm blue sea. The men in the
corvette watched in astonishment at what was happening on the flagship.

Encisco screamed conflicting orders. "Secure the
main hatch! Let go the anchors! Man the pumps!
Save everything!" The sight of supplies and trade
goods being ruined and of the ship breaking up made
him frantic. He had paid for all this. He would be
ruined! It was another of many instances when a
Spanish ship had foundered because a landsman was
in command.

Balboa, veteran of one foundering, led the men
and set an example by his coolness and strength. The
terrified horses could not be saved but the men did
recover dozens of swords, a little gunpowder and
some flour, bacon and armor.

In the growing darkness Indians watched the men

haul the scant supplies clear of the tide line. Camp was made near the ruins of San Sebastian and all that night the expedition huddled around a great campfire. By morning the morale of the men was low. The strongest kind of leadership was badly needed.

Again Encisco blundered. He could think only of recovering his loss by quickly getting gold. Donning full armor, which his slight frame could hardly support, he chose a war party of one hundred reluctant men. Balboa, Pizarro, Hurtado and other seasoned fighters were left to guard the corvette.

Before noon Encisco and his detachment were back on the beach. They had been met by a "superior force" and had retreated in "good order." Encisco glowered at his men. "I personally estimated the enemy at two thousand," he reported. But the veterans of the march would not tolerate the outlandish lie.

"*Compañeros!*" A wiry, dark-skinned sergeant appealed to the entire company at the water's edge. "We must face the facts. Otherwise we die." He raised his voice. "Today we were routed. One hundred of us chased like frightened babes, the *bachiller* as hysterical as a woman. And why lie? It was no force of two thousand. Nothing like it." The man paused for breath. His eyes lifted. "You, Lieutenant Balboa, will not think that what I have to say is possible. But I swear it. We were chased by *three* of these parrot-colored savages. I repeat: *uno, dos, tres.* I am ashamed." The sergeant spat at Encisco's feet. Two other men shouted confirmation. A rumble of discontent sounded in the ranks.

"Bachiller!" Balboa rose. The men quieted when he held up his big hands. "We are in peril," he said. "We must get food and shelter. We must show these people promptly that they deal with soldiers of Spain, not with runaway calves. Also, are we not here for gold?"

"Ha!" Encisco was about to fume and debate his position, but the sullen looks on all sides and the grim face of his stowaway made him change his line of attack. His legal mind told him to turn the tables. "You want trouble, Balboa," he declared. "You are a troublemaker. It's all very well for you to talk. Can you do anything except talk?"

"Yes." Balboa waved a hand around. "First, we should move from this place." He half turned and pointed to the opposite coast twenty miles in the distance. "Years ago I went ashore across this Gulf. We found a village that was abundant with food. The people did not use poison on their arrows. I say we should embark there now—this very day."

The men cheered the suggestion. Encisco was forgotten as willing hands loaded the *Chapinera* for the voyage to the other side of the Gulf of Uraba. And the *bachiller's* carping was ignored when they set up the new camp. To Balboa alone would the men listen. The lawyer waited. He let the stowaway give orders. He made no objection when the call was made for volunteers to march against a threatening force of savages led by their chief, Cemaco.

Spain's first victory on Tierra Firme came that day in late November of 1510. The men who remained behind heard the distant battle shouts and screams and the discharge of hand guns. Balboa, with Leoncico at his side, was in the van of an attack that routed a large native force. More than that, the raiders returned loaded with gold shields, masks, collars and crowns. Balboa's sword was stained; Leoncico showed a great gash on his flank. No lives had been lost.

At this point Encisco made his final mistake. He resumed command for the counting of the loot. He was in the forefront as stacks were piled, weighed and counted. Smiling in his oiliest fashion, rubbing his hands, Encisco announced they were richer by ten thousand pesos *de oro* (about $2,500.00) for the morning's work. He then told the assembled company how the plunder was to be divided.

Because of his heavy expenses, because he was their

Spain's first victory on Tierra Firme: November, 1510

officially appointed leader, and because the law allowed and prescribed . . . Encisco droned on. Finally he came to the astonishing conclusion that he would take 6,000 pesos! Everyone else would share alike—*twenty-five* pesos each!

A storm of protest broke. "Hang the cheating money-grubber! Up with him!" The men surged forward, wild with rage. Only the intervention of Balboa saved the lawyer's life. But the men would have no more of Encisco.

Someone called for Balboa to take command. Other voices took up the cry. They must have a new leader. Out of the babble of excitement came a show of order and a quick election. Unanimously Balboa was elected captain. Encisco screamed it was mutiny. History would call it the first town meeting on continental America, held sometime late in 1510.

"So be it!" Balboa towered above the nearest men. "I will be your captain. But I mean to be obeyed. My first order is that we commit no murder." He pointed to the cringing Encisco whose life he was sparing. "This man is a leech. He is incompetent and I would not feed him to my dog. But the hanging of him will be done in Spain. Back there he goes, with my personal report, by the first ship that sails."

Later, when he was alone with Balboa, Hurtado

spoke his mind. "You have made your first mistake, Captain," he said. "Better to have let the *compañeros* hang that fellow."

Balboa disagreed. "Keep in mind that I saved his life. In his place I would be everlastingly grateful."

Hurtado shrugged and walked away. The Captain was a strong and honest man. But in many ways he was a child.

6

Tales of Gold

The poor native village four miles inland from the desolate shores of Darien had been called "The Garrison" by Encisco. To Balboa the name meant nothing, for he and his men were starting here in the wilds with little more than faith and courage. Remembering that his long-delayed start to the New World had been from Seville, he rechristened the site after the madonna of that city, Santa Maria del Antigua. (This town, long since gone, was at the present border of Panama and Colombia.)

Balboa now took over with the greatest energy and determination. He had his knowledge of farming, building and organizing from the years at Hispaniola. He knew how to lead men and make friends with the Indians. And he knew what to avoid by remembering the antics of Bastidas and Encisco.

The first problem of the settlers was finding food. Hunting and fishing parties were organized while other detachments were sent to barter for cassava and fruit. A plaza was laid out and houses were built, native fashion: Floors and frames were laid on big rocks and the sides made of cane. Overhanging thatched roofs were woven from marsh grass.

To provide the barren settlement with needed equipment, Balboa dispatched the corvette *Chapinera* to Hispaniola with an order for a gold smelter, a church bell, forges, skillets, pots and arms. The money for these necessities came from his own share of the loot. Another shipment of treasure went to Diego Columbus with the request that he confirm Balboa's election as head of the colony. Also, an agent was sent to report the lay of the land at Santo Domingo and then proceed to Spain to secure the good will of King Ferdinand.

Exploration of the territory around Antigua revealed a fever-ridden jungle stretching from the mountains to the sea. Soon the armor rusted and clothing began to mold. The rivers were filled with crocodiles; the dreaded anaconda slithered along the gnarled limbs of trees and jaguars lurked near the water holes. At night the men were terrorized by vampire bats and flying cockroaches. As they felled trees during the humid days they were bitten by scorpions, mango flies and huge mosquitoes. One soldier had all his front teeth knocked out when a monkey hurled a coconut at him.

These pioneers were strong men. They could stand the torrential rains and the constant sweating which kept their sores from healing. But many soon began to show signs of breaking under the nerve-strain that came with the knowledge that they were a small force, alone and in danger of being slaughtered any night. Here Balboa came to the fore as leader.

"*Compañeros,*" he addressed the men, "we are almost ready to begin the conquest of this country. I promise that in three months' time the bets you make on these cockroach fights will be made with pesos *de oro,* not coppers."

After a cheer had interrupted him, Balboa continued: "We start immediately to train for our marches to the north where there is said to be much gold. We must learn to fight differently from the way men do on the fields in Europe. I will tell you what I learned at the Higuey campaign in Hispaniola."

The forays against the Indians of Cemaco, the chief who had been ousted from the coast, brought a knowledge of infiltration tactics to the Spanish soldiers. Until then they had used the ancient square formation. Balboa told them to forget what they had learned about drawing up in rigid order with set places for cavalry, harquebusiers, bowmen and foot troops. And they must leave behind most of their clanking, heavy armor.

The men went into battle wearing breeches, sandals and quilted cotton shirts which protected them against the Indians' darts, wooden swords and clubs. Marching in a crouch, single file, they descended silently and swiftly on the nearby villages. The dogs were released and on the enemy before he could pick them off with arrows or the black palm spears.

Rival natives were made allies with gifts of trinkets and did not mind seeing their ancient foes defeated. They led Balboa and his men along hidden trails until the lieutenants knew the terrain up from the Tanela, Atrato and Lajas rivers. Balboa was then able to concentrate on planning a large-scale campaign and drawing a map of the surrounding country.

The tales of captives, volunteers and returned expeditions were recorded and examined by the Captain, then discussed by his most reliable lieutenants.

These included Hurtado, Luis Botello, a future business partner, Andres de Valdarrabano, a rugged young notary, and the soldier Hernando Munzo. They heard of the Kingdom of Careta, four days' sail to the west. Inland lay Ponca and beyond that the richest domain of all, Comogra.

Within a few hundred miles, the report said, there were more than thirty separate nations, all enemies, all burdened with wealth. Later it developed that this population was greater than the total of all the Indians of North America. Balboa also heard rumors of some Other Sea to the south but his interest now was in conquest of the land. All that held him back was lack of arms and this shortage was relieved in April of 1511.

With the supplies from Hispaniola came the good news that Diego Columbus had appointed Balboa acting captain and had sent his recommendation to King Ferdinand. The future looked bright to the man who, less than a year before, had almost despaired of ever leaving Hispaniola.

But the months without supplies, and the delay in marching, had caused many of the soldiers to become restless and quarrelsome. It had even been necessary to build a jail to confine the few who openly questioned the authority of the man they had elected. The ringleader of these malcontents was Francisco Pizarro, and no one was surprised when an open break came between him and the Captain.

The first serious test of Balboa's command took place near noon one day after a skirmishing party had returned. Hernando de Arguello, a new and loyal friend, reported the trouble. "You will want to go to the plaza yourself," the soldier advised.

Balboa pushed aside a map he had been studying, pulled on a shirt and strode across the clearing. Two groups had formed around Pizarro who was talking in a loud, harsh voice.

Balboa frowned. Pizarro and six men had left town in the morning. One of the party was not present.

"Where is Francisco Hernan?" Balboa asked.

Pizarro shrugged. "He fell. We were attacked by some of Cemaco's savages."

"Did you bury him deep?"

"He was not dead."

"Do I hear you rightly?" Balboa's voice cut across the silent plaza. "Do you mean to say you left your *compañero* in that jungle alive?"

"He will not live long," Pizarro said. "I had myself and these others to consider." The black, close-set eyes were defiant. A few men nodded agreement.

"How far away is Hernan?" Balboa's bronzed face had become flushed. He worked his hands.

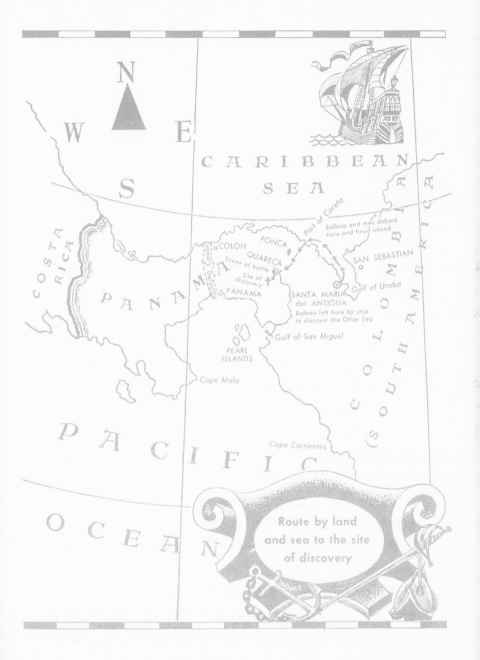

N

W ▲ E

S

CARIBBEAN

SEA

COSTA RICA

COLON

PONCA

Port of Careta

Balboa and men debark
here and head inland

PANAMA

Cordillera

QUARECA

Scene of battle

Site of
discovery

SAN SEBASTIAN

PANAMA

SANTA MARIA
del ANTIGUA

Balboa left here by ship
to discover the Other Sea

Gulf of Uraba

SOUTH AMERICA (COLOMBIA)

PEARL
ISLANDS

Gulf of San Miguel

Cape Mala

PACIFIC

Cape Corrientes

OCEAN

Route by land
and sea to the site
of discovery

"Maybe two hours. Follow our trail along the La-jas. You will find him dead by now." Pizarro turned to leave.

"One moment!" Balboa stepped a pace closer. The men moved back, sensing a fight. Pizarro paused with a surly, challenging stare.

"You will take your men and a litter," Balboa ordered. "I give you five hours—until sunset—to bring Hernan back here. See that he is alive."

"I do not have to obey that order!" Pizarro growled.

"True." Balboa hooked thumbs in his belt. "But let me tell you what will happen if you do not obey, or if you do not have Hernan here alive by sunset. The company will be assembled. Then you and I, Pizarro, will take up our swords. That fight will be to the death. *Now march!*"

Pizarro stared for a moment. Then his eyes lowered and he muttered an oath. "I will go," he said with ill humor, "but I cannot help it if the man dies. I cannot work miracles."

"That also is true," Balboa said angrily. "See that you keep it in mind. Do not wait until you face me with a sword to work some miracle. Go get your *compañero!*"

A few minutes before the sun was due to set the entire population of Antigua had gathered in the plaza where Balboa waited. But the crowd was disappointed. There would be no fight to the death. Pizarro led the way in from the trail; on the litter the wounded soldier still breathed.

Balboa had Hernan carried to his own house and called for hot water and salt. He waved away the surgeon who wished to bleed the injured man.

"We are not in Andalusia," Balboa said. He swabbed out the arrow wound, applied a salve of Indian root, and fixed a bandage. Hernan lived.

Pizarro, an ignorant and sensitive man, never forgave Balboa. He worked off his smoldering anger in the cruel maiming and killing of Indians. Disgruntled soldiers followed his example and these butchers were responsible for the spread of Spain's evil reputation in the New World.

After the incident of open insubordination, Balboa decided to get his men on the march and sent out scouts to Careta. They returned with the dampening news that the Cacique Chima had at his command two thousand troops. When the rains stopped these savages planned to wipe out the Spaniards.

Although incessant rain had made the land a bog Balboa chose a large detachment of his best men and sailed out of Antigua under cover of darkness. The Spaniards made a night landing at Careta with practiced skill and silently approached the village. At dawn they had the buildings surrounded. Dogs were set to be unleashed; hand guns were loaded and at the ready.

At daylight Balboa was surprised to see only women, children and old men in the village. Presently a scout brought word that the main army was engaged in fighting at the Kingdom of Ponca. The savages had been confident that the white men would not move until summer.

Chief Chima came forward prepared to meet death. The *compañeros* hungrily eyed the helpless people and their treasure. Here, with every advantage, with a chance to give his men some diversion, Balboa set the policy that made him the greatest of the *conquistadores.*

He jammed his sword into the ground, threw down his dagger, and came forward smiling with both hands raised. He embraced the Cacique. There were tears in the old man's eyes as he heard the Captain order his men to disarm and bring forward gifts of iron hatchets, beads, hawk's bells and colored glass.

Here at Careta Balboa made the first of many treaties. Chima agreed to send *naborias*—workers—to cultivate food for the settlers. He promised all the gold available and offered the services of his men as carriers. Finally, overcome by the kindness of the conqueror, he brought forth his most beautiful daughter, the princess Anayansi, and offered her as a slave.

Chima offered his most beautiful daughter as a slave

Here again Balboa rose to great heights, partly as a matter of policy, but mostly because he felt love touch him for the first time. He accepted Anayansi, not as a slave but as his ward.

In return for all he was given and promised Balboa agreed to march against the enemy tribe at Ponca and leave its chief forever defeated. Wasting no time, he led his troops out of Careta thē next morning.

With Leoncico at his side, Balboa led the charge into Ponca and routed the enemy. To show his force he had the village burned after taking quantities of gold. The word would now go out that he could be as fierce as he was kind.

While his men were in fighting mood Balboa decided to push on another one hundred and forty miles to the domain of Comogra whose chief commanded three thousand troops. He sent ahead some of Careta's men with an offer of peace.

Chief Comogra and his seven sons, dressed in ceremonial garments, met the Spaniards when they were still a day's march from the village. Instead of a spear the chief carried a ten-foot necklace with links made of pure gold. He draped it around Balboa's neck and promised a welcome never before accorded to any invading captain.

On the march into the capital village the chief's

oldest son attached himself to Balboa. He was a lad of sixteen, tall, lithe and muscular, and he was permitted to carry the Captain's sword. Leoncico, who had the remarkable ability of being able to distinguish between friendly and unfriendly Indians, nuzzled up to the boy, whose name was Ponquiaco.

The Spaniards were now used to rough and simple living, which made their surprise all the greater when they entered Comogra's jungle headquarters. The first thing to catch their attention was a huge, sprawling thatch-roofed palace. It measured four hundred and fifty feet in length and was almost three hundred feet wide. The open sides were supported by thick pillars and the entire structure was enclosed by a high wall of stone. But the greatest surprise came inside.

The first of many compartments was the Hall of Ancestors. Balboa cast a warning glance at the men nearest him as they gloated over the mummies of past rulers. These were bedecked in clothing to which gold disks and pearls had been sewn. The shriveled faces were hidden behind solid gold masks. As a setting for the ancestors there were vases, stands, statues and ornaments of priceless workmanship, silent evidence of generations of toil.

The Spaniards passed on, inspecting storerooms piled high with wines and foodstuffs, steaming

The first compartment was the Hall of Ancestors

kitchens, and then the banquet hall, where an elaborate feast took their minds off the gold.

During the meal Balboa questioned young Ponquiaco, who begged his father to let him go back to Antigua with the white men. Balboa liked the boy and added a hearty invitation to the lad's plea.

"But we must change your name," he told Ponquiaco. "It sounds too much like our word for 'almost nothing.' That is not you." Balboa thought for a moment and then said, "We will call you Carlos. How is that?"

The boy nodded and grinned. "You Tiba. Means Great Chief."

From that day on Carlos was never far from the Tiba. The boy stood fascinated when the Spaniards demolished a shield with shot from one of the hand muskets and demonstrated the tremendous force of a lead crossbow quarrel. This show was put on before a parley about gold was held.

When Balboa left Comogra he carried with him the greatest amount of treasure taken by anyone in the New World up to that time. The expedition returned to Antigua richer by $100,000.00. So great was the haul that Balboa paid little attention to new rumors of the Other Sea to the south. He was more interested in tales of a city of golden temples ruled by

a goddess. This was called Dabaibe and was said to
be in the mountains east of the Atrato River, about
one hundred miles from Darien.

While his men rested Balboa was married to Anayansi but he took no honeymoon. Instead he assembled seventy fresh soldiers and marched away to head
off a threat which would have erased Antigua and all
his gains.

Cemaco, whom Balboa had twice defeated, had
assembled five thousand natives. A spy brought word
that a pincers attack was imminent. Half the force
would come by land; the rest had a fleet of big war
canoes ready for a sea invasion. Balboa and his men
sacked two villages, then surrounded the invasion
supply base. He commandeered all food, arms and
canoes. The ringleaders were hanged and again there
was peace.

Balboa rested by urging his men and the Indians to
improve and strengthen the town. The population
now consisted of three hundred white men and ap-
proximately a thousand natives, with a sprinkling of
Africans who had been imported as slaves to Hispaniola. In addition to a church, the settlement boasted
one hundred houses, and logs had been laid along
the boggy trail to the bay to make a road.

When he was not working Balboa amused himself

by teaching Carlos Comogra the art of the sword. The boy was an apt pupil and brought back memories of the Tiba's own youth at Moguer.

Other memories, more recent and less pleasant, came crowding in on Balboa with the arrival of the next ship. The bad news came just as the year 1512 was drawing to a close.

A letter from his agent began with the good word that King Ferdinand had approved Balboa's appointment as captain at Darien some time before. "But last week," the letter continued, "His Majesty gave audience to a man who had many evil things to say about you. This man is a veteran explorer, Indian fighter and captain, and HRH was said to have been impressed, more by the record than appearances. The man is a *bachiller* named Martin Fernandez de Encisco . . ."

Balboa crumpled the letter in his fist before flinging it to the ground, and then stamped out of the house and around to the back garden, where he could be alone. It was unbelievable! Encisco! "An Indian fighter, explorer, captain." *Caramba!* Hurtado had been right. He should have let the men hang Encisco.

Until long after dark Balboa paced the garden, head down, arms locked behind his back. What would happen now? There would be officials, investigators and more lawyers. No doubt Encisco had the ear of Bishop Fonseca, who was in charge of Indies Affairs. Now, just as he was making progress, he would be recalled or demoted. After all these years of waiting his golden opportunity . . .

"Tiba!"

Balboa started. His hand went automatically to his side. Then he laughed when he saw Carlos standing near the dark vines. Preoccupation was bad for one, the Captain reflected. It was not a good way of spending time if one wanted to stay alive in this primitive country.

"You are troubled, Tiba," the boy said, coming closer. "I know. Your King want more gold."

"That is not far wrong, my boy. But do not let it concern you. Have you practiced with the weights today? We must strengthen those wrists if you are to master the sword."

Carlos nodded and looked at the ground. "You do much for me, Tiba—for everyone—so now I tell you of gold. Great gold."

"Not the golden temples of Dabaibe?"

"No, Tiba. That is legend. Even Indians not believe that. I tell of the Other Sea."

"We have heard of this sea to the south," Balboa

said. "But our greatest geographers know nothing of it. However, go ahead."

Carlos shrugged. "I tell only what I see and what wise, very old soothsayers believe."

"Good." Balboa stretched himself out on an Indian hammock slung between the side of the house and a palm tree.

"Six suns," Carlos pointed south, "maybe more for large army, is the great sea. Goes far away. I have seen. Have seen on waters ships with white wings. Mighty as your ships, Tiba." Carlos paused and frowned. "Other sea is . . . belong to people of the Sun. Have more gold than any. Walk on gold floor. Live in gold hut. Tiba's people use iron. Sun people use gold. It is true."

"Why haven't I heard more about this gold, Carlos?"

"Too few men. Your King send thousand men, thousand guns. Then maybe."

"You said it was six suns' march?"

"Yes, Tiba. But march is through land of Quareca. Has mighty army. Mighty Cacique Torecha never let white man pass."

That night Balboa lay awake until late. Could it be true? Could there be another body of water like the Ocean Sea? It was not shown on the *mappemonde,* or world map, of Cosa. If he acted on what Carlos had told him, he would be taking the word of an Indian boy against that of the best scholars in Europe. Yet, those scholars had been wrong when Christopher Columbus was begging for ships. Balboa believed the boy.

7

Discovery

Like a good captain Balboa began to examine everyone in Antigua who might have knowledge of this Other Sea. Veteran raiders and old men repeated Carlos Comogra's story. No, it was not a *bahia* or large gulf. The tides there rose and fell eighteen feet every day. Yes, great ships had been seen on the distant horizon. Would not the Sun people, who ate from plates of gold, own a mighty fleet?

Shipmasters then in port—Cristobal Serrano, Juan

de Ledesma and Alonso de Quiroga—were skeptical. They had all heard talk of a strait and it was said that even now Captain Juan Cabot was searching for it. And a certain Ferdinand Magellan was pestering European monarchs for ships so that he could discover a southern passage to Cathay.

Now that Balboa was firmly convinced in his own mind, his first act was one of loyalty to his King. With a cloth wrapped around his arm to keep perspiration from dripping onto the parchment, he wrote the date —January 20, 1513—and began a lengthy letter to King Ferdinand.

Balboa first traced the history of Darien. He told how Hojeda and Nicuesa between them had lost eight hundred men; how natives had been robbed and murdered; how self-seeking incompetents like Encisco became the cause of misery and rebellion. He offered his own record as proof that an able and sincere captain could accomplish far more than any lawyer, notary or court favorite.

After setting down what he knew of the country and what he had heard of the great ocean to the south, Balboa requested cooperation. "Your Very Royal Highness should command," he wrote, "that certain provisions be supplied so that the land can be thoroughly explored and its secrets learned and that the Other Sea may be claimed in your name."

The letter asked for one thousand veterans from Hispaniola, artisans to build ships, armorers to keep the guns in repair, and more military equipment. It specified the best types of guns and told of plans for forts, roadways, ships and future cities.

Balboa ended with a plea in behalf of his men, asking that they be given a greater share of the plunder in future because of the great risks they took. "Your Royal Highness knows that nothing done unwillingly is ever done well."

The letter, along with a gift of some prize pearls, was entrusted to Sebastian de Ocampo who had "connections" in Spain. Balboa was so confident of having all his requests granted within four months that he began preparations for his march to the Other Sea.

Between January and May fifty large houses were built to provide for the troops the King would send. Shelters were thrown up to store a collection of *habas,* the big covered baskets the Indians used on a march. Clay was dug to make a supply of the tall water jugs, called *torebas.* While provisions were being assembled men began strengthening the defenses of Antigua lest Cemaco organize another raid. When Balboa was not working on maps or checking armor his thoughts were on the Other Sea. It was just as well that he did not know what was happening in Spain.

Balboa's letter was delivered to King Ferdinand but the emissary, Sebastian de Ocampo, failed to get an audience. There was great excitement over the news of the Other Sea. Portugal had moved far ahead of Spain, circling Africa to open trade with the Orient. Now was the chance to sail westward. More important even was this news of gold.

Then Balboa's clever enemies had a talk with Ferdinand who, since the death of his wife, had been at best a weak ruler. Was His Royal Highness not aware of the significance attached to the discovering of a new ocean? Did he propose to have this historic deed done by a nobody like Balboa? Who would witness the event, a handful of swashbucklers?

King Ferdinand was won over. He selected Pedro Arias de Avila, a seventy-year-old courtier who was known as Pedrarias. Here was a man familiar with protocol, court etiquette and royal functions. He would have at his command two thousand of the best people and would sail in a fleet of twenty-two ships.

Balboa learned of the new plans in mid-August when a ship from Spain arrived carrying an impressive scroll of an earlier date which gave him the royal commission as Captain at Darien. Someone had forgotten to cancel this, and no official word had come about his replacement. There was still time to act.

While his lieutenants were being summoned Balboa paced his back garden. What, he wondered, had happened to His Majesty? Surely his letter had been plain in telling of the difficulty of a march to the Other Sea. It should be obvious that this was not work for a soft court fob. Important personages would find it heavy going through jungle country. He was hurt by King Ferdinand's decision but his loyalty did not waver. He could see the conniving hand of Encisco and he was determined that the lawyer would not rob him of the honor of being the first to look upon the waters of the Other Sea. He and the *compañeros* had earned that right.

"The time has come to march," Balboa told his officers. He explained to them what had happened in Spain and how they all stood to be robbed of the glory and gold of the Other Sea. He then patiently listened to objections.

"It is true we are poorly equipped," he admitted. "I would prefer three times any force we can muster, every man equipped with the best. Also, there should be supply bases, reliefs and more skilled artisans. But consider again!" Balboa's eyes gleamed. "Suppose we had all the trappings and were not men? *Hombre!* Gold and honor are waiting. We have strength and the resolve. I mean to lead our company to this Other Sea before any other captain."

Every man in Antigua volunteered as hasty preparations were made. One hundred and ninety of the strongest soldiers were chosen after a rigid examination by the Captain. He had never abandoned a man on the march and this time he could afford no stragglers. "We will be followed night and day once we leave Ponca," he warned. "The savages will be at our flanks like hungry hyenas."

The five hundred people in Antigua hauled supplies and arms down the three miles to the beach for loading aboard the corvette *Chapinera* and nine canoes. A messenger was sent overland to tell Carlos Comogra to march a thousand Indian carriers to the port of Careta.

On the last day of August, Mass was said in the open and at dawn the next morning the expedition embarked. Balboa kissed Anayansi good-bye and waded out to the small ship. The little fleet caught the offshore breeze and stood away toward Punta

Goleta. At the Captain's side crouched Leoncico.

Heavy rain squalls lashed the coast of Careta as the ship and canoes worked into the anchorage. Carlos was there with his men to help unload. Gear and provisions were soaked before they could be dragged into shelters and the embarkation beach became a bog. Like an ill omen the downpour continued through the night. The dogs howled and in the morning the first complaints were heard.

"What do your scouts hear, Carlos?" Balboa asked as he and his men prepared to break camp in the morning.

"Nothing good, Tiba," the boy said. Carlos had mastered Spanish now and he had filled out in eight months. He was looked up to by the people of Comogra because of his skill with the sword.

"Does that chief, Torecha, still intend to fight me?"

"Yes, Tiba. More than one thousand already wait. Scouts are outside of Ponca to watch."

Balboa laughed and patted Carlos on the back. Leoncico shook his head, tongue lolling. It had been weeks since he had been in battle.

Through two days of torrential rains the brave cavalcade pushed on to Ponca. Soldiers and natives hacked at palms of many kinds and crushed back thick bamboo shoots to widen the path for the carriers. Troops of monkeys followed the march, chattering and throwing coconuts.

At night clearings were made in the tangle of air plants, vines and gray hanging moss. The men made smoky fires of sodden wood and sweated as they heard the eerie cry of the wild *ochi*—the panther. At dawn they would awaken groggy and covered with welts to see unhealthy mists rising from the wet forest floor.

The weather and fear sapped their strength before they climbed the ridge into Ponca. Here Balboa called a halt to determine which of the men were coming down with fever.

"Would you not wait four moons?" Carlos asked. "The rains will then stop."

"No!" Balboa was firm. "If we cannot stand it now we may never have the chance again." He was thinking of the fleet bringing his successor. There was no telling when it would arrive off Antigua.

But Balboa did call a nine-day halt. Twelve men were sent back to Antigua and half the others went to Careta. The remaining eighty-nine rested for the struggle ahead. During that time scouts continued to bring in ominous reports. Every day eager warriors

from the east and west were joining the Quareca nation, including cannibal Caribs who had been promised any Christian they took. When Balboa saw the
compañeros growing restless he gave the order to
break camp.

The first day's march out of Ponca was a night-
mare. In single file, stretched out for more than a
mile, the party descended through rotting, swampy
jungle to the bank of the Morti River. They trudged
along the muddy, yellow bank, then undressed and
waded across, clothes piled on shields and bucklers
balanced on their heads. Soldiers slashed at crocodiles
and water snakes; a native screamed, then was
dragged under and never seen again.

Again they pushed into the steaming half-light of
jungle forest. Overhead the rain beat a wild tattoo on
the roof of stiff leaves. Screams from birds arose as
the men brushed past slimy, bile-green vegetation.

With Balboa marched Carlos and Leoncico. A few
paces behind, unbothered by the climate, came Nuflo
de Olano, the only African in the expedition.

Midway in the first week out of Ponca, as the party
neared its goal and the intercepting army of Quareca,
ten men collapsed under a torrid sun at noon. Litters
were made from spears and shirts. Balboa took his

They pushed into the steaming half-light of jungle forest

own armor from a carrier and made him a stretcher bearer. The *compañeros* followed their commander's example. But before sundown five more men fainted, and through the night others came down with the fever.

Balboa urged the company on to the next encampment, dodging back and forward through the ranks with jokes, words of encouragement to the men, and appeals to their pride. In one more day they would reach the mountains from which they could see the Other Ocean. In one more day they would also meet the enemy.

But the enemy was even closer than Balboa had suspected. Dreadful evidence of how close was shown that very night.

One of Carlos' scouts could be heard screaming before he burst into the clearing. Blood streamed down both sides of his face, and over his arms and sides. His ears had been sliced off and were tied on a chain of gold around his neck. Carlos held the man while another native lit the root of a certain plant. When the scout inhaled the smoke the pain was dulled and he could talk. Carlos interpreted.

"A message from the Cacique Torecha, Tiba. For you. Torecha says he will capture you himself. Then you will have special treatment for all to witness. Do you wish to know it?"

"Go ahead!" Balboa could see the curious men moving closer.

Carlos glanced at the maimed scout who had been bandaged and now stared glassily under the influence of the narcotic. "You are to be fastened to the ground, Tiba," the boy said. "Then gold will be melted over the hot coals. Your mouth will be pried open. Torecha will pour the molten gold down your throat. The same with your officers."

"A terrible death," Balboa said. "But first it will be necessary to capture me."

"Maybe that won't be impossible," said one of the soldiers. "The sick list is now up to twenty-five." Balboa recognized the shifty-eyed fellow. It was always easy to tell Andres de Garabito from the ugly scar which had been carved on his cheek at Hispaniola by Cortes.

"A lot of us think it's time to turn back, Captain," another man said. "This is folly. We will be cut down like reeds or put to one of these tortures by that heathen devil."

"Assemble the company!" Balboa gave the order to Hurtado. This was to be the big test. He could not blame sick men who had been away from home for twenty-three days for feeling dispirited about a lengthy trek across to the Other Sea. He must convince them it would be worth it.

"You all know I am not a man who lies to gain his way," Balboa began when the last stragglers had gathered around. "First I am going to tell you what we have to gain after only one more short march." He pictured a quick defeat of the enemy and the gathering of a huge amount of gold. Then he told of the Other Sea whose discovery they could talk about the rest of their lives. They would go on to relieve the peace-loving tribes on those shores of more treasure and return to Antigua richer than most Spanish nobles.

"All this is true and I swear it," Balboa said with great conviction. "But *compañeros,* I will be honest and let you see the other side of the coin. Consider what will happen if we now retreat, carrying litters. This Torecha will be on us like a wolf. If we show fear, by nightfall tomorrow those who do not fall will be the victims of slow torture. Afterward, your wives and children will be taken."

Balboa paused and picked up his sword. Leoncico growled. "One more thing for you to consider, *com-*

pañeros," he said as though a vote were to be taken. "I do not seek, ever, to influence just by mere words. You have seen me fight. You know I have served under the great Juan Ponce de Leon. So I know whereof I speak when I say *this:* I can defeat the Cacique Torecha. I know a way. I doubt if it will cost a single life. But I cannot do this without you. You men control our destiny: to die in shame, or to win a great victory and acquire gold. Let me hear if any will follow me."

A spontaneous cheer blasted the darkening jungle. If there were any protests they were drowned out by the revived, enthusiastic men. Everything to gain and nothing to lose! It was simple.

As though to bless the new determination the explorers next day burst from the steaming jungle onto a plateau where the air seemed clean and crisp after the cloying lowlands. Ten miles in the distance the valley ended in a thick forest above which rose a spur of blue-gray mountains.

"There is the viewing place of the Other Sea, Tiba," said Carlos. "From the height you can see it. Below, in the woods, is Torecha's army. Listen!"

Faintly Balboa could hear the beat of war drums. He scanned the terrain which loomed as a great bowl whose sides were jungle forests. He smiled slowly and called for Hurtado, Munzo, Martin and Pizarro. His eyes were held by the ridge.

"Francisco Pizarro," Balboa said when the lieutenants had assembled, "let us forget whatever differences exist between us. You are now my comrade-in-arms. I want you to lead twenty men to an ambush before dawn tomorrow. You may kill as many as you wish of these cannibals."

"That order I like, Captain," said Pizarro. He hitched his breeches and spat, a mean grin spreading over his cruel face.

Hurtado was assigned another detachment. There would be an east and a west infiltration. The two parties would wear no armor and would take most of the dogs and hand guns. Native carriers disguised in helmets and breastplates would march down the valley with Balboa at their head.

The encircling troops slipped out of camp at three o'clock in the morning just before the moon set. The clatter of maracas and the heathenish chant of the native battle dance drowned out any sounds of their movement.

Before daybreak Balboa selected fifty delighted Indians who felt more than rewarded when allowed to don the Spanish armor. The men unable to fight numbered thirty, so this main body had only twenty *compañeros*. They also had Leoncico, now wearing a gold collar and on the list to draw a lieutenant's pay. In battle he was the equal of ten ferocious men.

The first rays of a blazing sun peeked over the mountains on his left when Balboa called out the order to march. As he took his place at the head of his party with his dog, it was seen that he wore no helmet. It was an obvious challenge to Torecha, this flaunting of the blond hair and beard of the conqueror whom Torecha hoped to take alone and torture.

By seven o'clock the party wound down the last trail to the plain and drew up to march in a rough square. Bright sunlight lit the plain and glistened on light-green and yellow groves of banana trees that fringed the forest.

In less than an hour Balboa and his party were close to the tangle of multi-colored vines. Near the fringe the chatter of nervous monkeys and the shrieks of scolding birds revealed the whereabouts of the overconfident enemy.

At fifty paces from the ambush Balboa and his

dog separated from the soldiers and natives who formed a neat battle square. Carlos covered the Captain. Somewhere behind the natives Pizarro and Hurtado should be ready.

Balboa stopped short and raised his hand. Then he leaned over, slapped the dog on the flank and, as he snapped his fingers, hoarsely whispered: *"Santiago!"*

Leoncico threw back his scarred head. The yellow body quivered and strained as his voice lifted in a wild howl that carried through the hills for half a mile.

The call had not died away when it was answered by the other dogs. Then came the shouts—*"Santiago! Adalante!"*—followed by the clash of swords, the whine of crossbow quarrels, and the screams of Indians. The Spaniards were outnumbered ten to one, but they had the dogs and weapons.

Torecha raced out of the forest at the head of twenty men. A great horde followed, then halted to turn and do battle with the charging *compañeros* who had surrounded them.

Balboa ran forward, sword blade flashing in the morning sun. The big Cacique waved his throwing stick, ready to launch the *vara,* the small rod tipped with flint which could skewer a man. Torecha's face was hideous with paint and tattoos.

Balboa's attack was lightning fast. His blade leapt out and cut the native weapon in half. The Cacique bounded to one side. A great brown hand now aimed a knife at the Captain's neck.

Assured that he was covered by the ripping, charging Leoncico and by Carlos who held a crossbow, Balboa disarmed Torecha. While the Cacique was still jabbering, Balboa sidestepped and threw down his sword, prepared for barehanded combat.

In the meantime, Pizarro and Hurtado had almost immobilized six hundred savages. The Spaniards were taking no captives and the din of screams rose to a horrible crescendo.

Now the two big leaders, Balboa and Torecha, moved toward each other, arms bent, legs tense. Carlos held his breath; Leoncico dropped a dead native and waited, poised. Torecho suddenly drew back, his hand whipping to his loincloth and jerking out a murderous, stubby knife.

Carlos had seen the Tiba fight with the sword, had seen him cleave a man from head to middle with one stroke, and had learned countless wrestling holds from him. But never had he watched such fast and powerful movements as the Captain displayed now. Suddenly Torecha screamed. His right arm had been broken. The knife he had been holding landed in a bush. Then the big brown man went hurtling into the air, and when he came down he lay still. His neck had been broken.

In less than half an hour of fierce fighting six hundred Indians were slain. As Balboa had predicted, the Spaniards did not suffer a single fatality. But the strain of battle brought down many who had been on the verge of fever. When the company marched into the village of Quareca only sixty-seven men were in shape to continue.

Balboa rallied the sound *compañeros* and started the short final march. Swords still dripped; clothing was soaked with blood; breathing was short. But they must push onward.

Fifty paces from the summit of the bald hill Balboa motioned the men to halt. His eyes briefly met those of Pizarro. He whistled to Leoncico, then turned and began the deliberate trek upward.

When his head came almost level with the summit, Balboa paused and took a deep breath. The bright sun overhead cast his shadow just before him.

The years slipped away for an instant. He felt again the exhilaration of youth. Then he mounted slowly.

The view that opened suddenly drove Balboa to his knees. There, far below, reaching endlessly to the south, lay the calm blue waters of the Other Sea. It was true! Balboa gazed transfixed at a great body of water never before seen by a white man. For a certainty, he thought, that placid ocean must be as boundless as eternity. And even as he continued to gaze, Balboa realized that four thousand years of knowledge had abruptly changed. Every globe in Europe was wrong; every learned scholar of history had been mistaken. And he, Vasco Núñez de Balboa, of Jerez de los Caballeros, was the first to know this.

The men who crept up the hill at his hand signal heard Balboa sob with joy in a hoarse, tear-choked voice:

"*El Mar! El Mar del Sur!* The Sea. The South Sea!"

The powerful swordsman and captain was so excited he was incoherent. While he embraced Carlos Comogra, the equally excited Leoncico yapping at his feet, Balboa gave conflicting orders about erect-

ing a cross, saying Mass, and singing the *Te Deum.*
He belabored Valdarrabano to get the names of all
present on parchment.

And thus the greatest ocean of the earth, the Pacific Ocean, was discovered at ten o'clock on the
morning of the twenty-fifth day of September in
the year 1513, according to the official record, although some say it may have been the twenty-sixth
or twenty-seventh day.

Scouting parties were sent ahead to prepare for
the simple christening ceremonies. On September
29th Balboa and twenty-six men walked to the beach
at what is now the Gulf of San Miguel. They tasted
the salty water and waited until two o'clock in the
afternoon for the *marea alta,* the high tide. Balboa
donned full armor. In one hand he held his sword,
in the other a tattered silk banner. He waded in up
to his knees and claimed the ocean as he sloshed
back and forth, eyes lifted, proclaiming in a voice
deep and loud:

*"Long live the most high and mighty sovereigns
Don Fernando and Dona Juana, rulers of Castile,
and Leon, and Aragon . . ."* As he slowly marched
he claimed the sea *"for now and in all time while*

the earth turns, and until the universal judgment of all mankind."

Balboa's christening ended with the warning: *"If any other Prince or Captain, Christian or Infidel, pretends any rights to this Sea, I am the man who will contradict him."*

Balboa waded in and claimed the ocean

8

Deposed

The cheering, weary discoverers of the South Sea swaggered into Antigua on January 19th, 1514. They had marched and fought five months in the rain without the loss of a single life. Their treasure in gold and pearls would be worth one hundred and fifty thousand dollars today.

Balboa's face looked gaunt, and hidden among the blond hairs of his head and beard were sprinklings of gray. Otherwise there was nothing to tell that he had suffered an attack of malaria on the trek back.

As the gold was weighed and distributed, the heroes told of their adventures after the christening of the South Sea:

At the land of Chape they extracted a large tribute from the woman ruler. They climbed inland to Cuquera and made a peaceful conquest, then doubled back to take canoes whose paddles were studded with pearls. There, and farther up the coast, Balboa collected four hundred and fifty of the gems and had pointed out to him the Pearl Islands off the coast. Beyond the head of the Mahagual River the Spaniards engaged the evil Cacique of Pacra in combat and then pushed ahead to meet the richest lord of the country, the powerful Tubanama who lived in a six-hundred-foot hut with eighty wives. The Cacique and his harem were held as hostages until Balboa's carriers were loaded with plunder. Then, anxious to get word of the discovery and gold to King Ferdinand, Balboa headed for Antigua on a litter. In his wake were the caciques of twelve kingdoms who called him "Elder Brother" or "Father." Young men deserted their tribes to accompany the Spaniards and named Balboa "Warrior of the Sun."

Gold and pearls were loaded aboard the ship *Buen Jesus* along with the official documents of discovery.

Balboa wrote out another lengthy report of his activities which he hoped would earn him the grati-
tude of the King and a post on the other side of
the Isthmus after his replacement. He was thinking
then of the Pearl Islands and of the great Sun Empire to the south. He had even made plans by summer for another expedition to the newly discovered
ocean. Then the new governor, Pedrarias, arrived
with his fleet.

No one was prepared for any such arrival as that
of the Splendid Armada. The fleet of twenty-two sail
was sighted off the coast late in June and ranged up
to the anchorage on the twenty-ninth day of that
month. Decks were crowded with men, women and
children. The flagship was resplendent in gilt and
flew a seventy-foot crimson pennant from her main
mast truck. Word came ashore that Balboa should
appear, unarmed, at ten o'clock the next morning.

From dawn until the hour appointed for the official entry, barges plied between the fleet and shore.
Some of Balboa's men, together with Indians and
curious animals, watched from behind the jungle
fringe. They gaped as they saw two thousand people disembark, followed by horses, swine and supplies. The *compañeros* had all but forgotten what
multi-colored satins, silks, damask and brocades

Then the new governor arrived with his Splendid Armada

looked like. To many the beautiful women, the haughty cavaliers, the dressed-up children, were vague memories suddenly come to life. Nor was that the end of what they saw to astonish them. There were many varieties of fighting men, at least twenty-five priests, and many African slaves. Royal captains rode back and forth on horses in ornate housings; men were being given places according to their importance.

When the people of the armada had been assembled, the new Governor came ashore with his wife and the big dark-haired bishop, Juan de Quevedo. A trumpet sounded. Other trumpets blared and drums began to roll. The signal was given for Balboa and his men to emerge from the jungle.

Pedrarias sat his horse easily and looked ahead with an air of arrogance. In his seventy years he had gained many honors both in the field and in court. Thanks to an inheritance and his wife's connections he had risen to great favor.

The shrewd eyes of an accomplished politician watched the approaching men. Pedrarias waited. A big, sagging man with a prominent nose and thick, leathery lips, he felt pleased and important. His careful plans were working out to perfection. This appointment would mean that the generations to come must always honor him as the discoverer of the South Sea. So far as he was concerned, the blond giant now approaching with his company of ill-dressed ruffians had merely done the spade work.

The drums and trumpets stilled and voices faded when Pedrarias raised a hand. Balboa faced him, bronzed, confident and dressed as usual in an open-necked shirt, sandals and faded breeches. Pedrarias passed down a scroll which Balboa opened to read.

Purple-clad Bishop Quevedo looked approvingly at the big Captain. He made the sign of the Cross to the *compañeros* who were boldly eying the women or looking with scorn at the velvet scabbards of the courtiers. Pedrarias addressed a sharp word to his young wife which caused her to look away from the Captain.

"I make Your Excellency welcome," said Balboa, returning the document. "But you need not be bothered about the discovery of the South Sea. My men and I have already been there. Word of my christening must by now have reached His Royal Highness."

Pedrarias could not answer. His years showed as slack skin quivered under his chin. He trembled with rage. He was too late, too late even to change the document.

Balboa forced himself to smile down the line of whispering people: the officials and their pushing wives; the royal captains who had seen little or no combat; gold-hungry fobs now suddenly robbed of glory; sultry-eyed women who turned up their noses at the *compañeros*. There was scorn even on the faces of the well-fed lackeys. Wait, he thought, until they have been in Antigua one week. His smile became genuine when he caught the eyes of the children, all admiration for him and his men.

"How far is it to the city?" Pedrarias finally found his voice.

"A short journey of four miles, Excellency," Balboa said with a smile. "Shall I lead the way?"

As he was about to set off, Balboa's eyes picked out a familiar figure who was leering at him. *Caramba!* There stood Encisco! And he was no mere lawyer now; he wore the insignia of Constable. At his command he had three musketeers, two crossbow men, two fishermen, two huntsmen and a miller and his wife. Here was trouble.

Balboa turned and walked toward the jungle while the trumpets and drums accompanied the chanting of the priests. For two hours the procession sweated and stumbled over the rough trail, voices becoming more irritable with each step. The new-comers were stung and scratched; the mounted officers were made ridiculous when monkeys bombarded them with coconuts and mangoes. Tempers were held in check only because their owners expected comfort shortly. Then they entered the plaza and saw the rude houses.

Where were the marble palaces? Where was the main city? Two thousand people were shocked, bitterly disappointed and then loud in their criticism.

"I was given to understand," said Pedrarias tartly, "that this was a considerable city, the largest on the Tierra Firme."

"You are in rough country, Excellency. What we have is shelter. You will become accustomed to simple things. Look!" Balboa pointed to the suddenly darkened sky. He grinned at the demanding throng in the plaza, their fine clothes already ripped or stained. He beckoned Pedrarias and his aides to shelter under the thatched eaves of his house.

A splattering of big drops caused the people to look around for cover. Then the tropical rain descended like a solid sheet of water. Before the new-comers could push into people's houses they were drenched. White taffeta was splattered with mud;

soft, colored leather shoes sank in the mire. Encisco and his entourage raced for the shelter of Balboa's porch to join the Governor.

Inside, Pedrarias at first put on his oiliest manner. The wily politician knew how to make the best of things. He flattered Balboa and drew him out. He even had him dictate a long memorandum. Then the Governor called in Encisco with his six armed guards. As the interview seemed about to end Pedrarias abruptly changed. From having been suave in his manner he became grim. The aged face became foxlike. Then rage took over.

"You blunderer!" Pedrarias snarled. "You great fool! Have you no sense of decorum?"

Balboa looked over at the smirking Encisco and his bodyguard. Coolly he faced the old man. "Kindly instruct me, Excellency."

"That I will, since you seem too stupid to see what you have done. This Other Sea—this ocean— should have been left for *me* to discover. Your job was to direct the laborers here, to build suitable dwellings and perhaps a road part way to the Other Sea. But making a discovery! Don't you know your place?"

Balboa looked at the shaking, haughty old man. He thought of the sloughing he and his men had done through the jungle, of those whose strength had been sapped by fever, of the fight with Torecha. He shrugged and checked his anger.

"Excellency," he said, this time without respect, "as I told you before, this is a rough land. I have made it my home long enough to know. As for knowing my place, I am a *hidalgo* and if the truth be examined, better blood flows in my veins than in your own. But enough of that." Balboa paused and looked steadily at the imported Governor. "The plain fact is that you could not have made the march. Not even with a thousand troops such as you now command."

"You are the only captain in all the Kingdom who could have done so?" Pedrarias asked sarcastically. "You alone can defeat these heathens?"

"That is not what I said." Balboa smiled as his eyes met Encisco's. "These natives are not so easy to subdue. The *bachiller* knows. I recall a force under his command being routed by three of these heathens."

"Mind your libel," Encisco stormed. "I warned you. I'll have the law on you. I am here to see that you . . ."

"Quiet!" Pedrarias folded his shaking hands. "Balboa," he snapped, "you are a troublemaker. You are now under arrest. Seize him, guards! To jail with him!"

Balboa was jailed, then tried before one of the armada judges. The principal witness against him was Encisco, who lay claim to gold due him from all of the expeditions. Balboa lost his house, all of his savings, and most of his servants. His "resedencia" was then proclaimed. It meant he could neither leave Antigua nor take any part in activities there. He was as much a prisoner as he had been at Hispaniola, and again Encisco was his jailer.

There now began the rapid disintegration of all the good Balboa had accomplished. The first step of the new rulers was to make slaves of the Indians. Fifteen hundred *naborias* who had worked willingly in the fields were now branded and made to wear chains. Expeditions were organized for the purpose of sacking the friendly kingdoms for gold and bringing back captives who could be sold. Pedrarias had his own reasons for all this. He wanted the men to get gold so that they could buy the warehouse food he was selling.

Typical of the expeditions was one led by a nephew of Pedrarias with Encisco second in command. The force numbered four hundred and fifty men, all equipped with the best of harquebuses and bows. They advanced only fifteen miles before they were beaten. Another party of the same number marched on Careta under the cruel Captain Juan de Ayora, Pedrarias's first in command. By the time he returned empty-handed and with many dead, word of the Spaniards' cruelty had spread to every Indian nation. The Spaniard was now an enemy. Many were ambushed; little more gold came into Antigua. The only reason the savages did not descend on Antigua was the presence of Balboa, the *compañeros,* and "the dog," meaning Leoncico.

Carlos Comogra came at the height of the trouble to say his good-byes to Balboa and Anayansi. His father had been killed by the newly arrived Spaniards. He was going home to become Chief.

The *compañeros* heard later that Ayora had sacked Comogra and had taken Carlos prisoner but that the boy had escaped and "was killed in a swordfight with a soldier." Balboa very much doubted if any soldier of the armada could match his pupil. And Anayansi was sure they would see Carlos again.

As Pedrarias continued his reign of terror among the Indians, he and his cohorts began a system of cheating the settlers and their own people. Supplies and food were cornered and prices boomed. Before long people were starving. Then a new and terrible disaster struck Antigua.

Two months after the arrival of the armada plague suddenly broke out. It was the dread *modorra,* worse than bubonic plague and typhus together. People became drowsy, then had fits, and dropped dead in the streets. The disease was highly contagious, so staying in the settlement meant almost certain contamination. On the other hand, leaving meant death at the hands of Indians. They, like the original settlers, seemed immune to the *modorra.*

In the first month one hundred of Pedrarias's people died. The next few weeks saw the toll mount at a terrifying pace. By fall seven hundred persons had been stricken and the others fought for space aboard departing ships.

In his first six-months report Pedrarias did not mention the *modorra* nor did he write about his difficulties with the Indians. And he omitted any reference to gold. The once fat treasury was empty; the colony was in debt for 16,000 pesos. The only favorable news the Governor could send the King was that the young fruit trees were doing well and that the happy people had played games on Christmas.

Balboa also wrote through the months as he waited

for his "resedencia" to be lifted. He smuggled his letters out and some of them finally reached ailing King Ferdinand. That monarch realized he had made a grave mistake, and he tried now to correct it.

Early in 1515 two ships arrived which should have brought some word to Balboa. But there was silence from headquarters where Pedrarias processed all dispatches.

The master of one of the ships was Andres Nino, a nephew of Balboa's boyhood friend Francisco. The young Captain of the *Santa Maria de la Consolacion* sought out Balboa and said he had heard rumors there was mail for him.

When Balboa made inquiries, however, he was rebuked by the Governor. Weary and disillusioned, he might have done nothing had he not been shocked into action. A cruel tragedy awakened in him the fighting spirit he had shown so often before. Leoncico was poisoned.

The entire settlement felt uneasy when Balboa was told that his dog had been found dead in the plaza. The crowd fell back as the *conquistador* knelt beside his old friend. Leoncico had died in agony, his throat paralyzed. He had been chained to a tree so that he could not seek his master.

When Balboa returned from the jungle where he

buried the dog he pushed unseeing through the crowd. Ayora was there with the guard but he was not saying anything. On hand were the *compañeros* and the veteran jungle officers who had marched to the Other Sea.

Balboa walked to his old house. The Governor's guards took one look at him and scurried away from the door. Balboa strode slowly in to face Pedrarias. At sight of him the old man quailed. A coward at heart, he sensed that his end might be near. The killing of the dog had been foolish.

"I am leaving this place," Balboa announced. "I will commandeer the ships in the roadstead and sail for Spain."

Pedrarias checked his surprise. He drummed nervously on the big desk behind which he sat studying documents.

"I am taking my case to the King," Balboa continued in a menacing tone. "I will do so before you can advise any of your agents."

"Well . . ." Pedrarias tried to spar for time.

"Quiet!" Balboa ordered. "I am not going in rags. And I will have my audience before any schemers can interfere. I will march on the court as I did on the Other Sea. His Majesty can judge if I am a fit captain or one who should be ignored."

Balboa's dog had been found dead in the plaza

"Please!" Pedrarias put on his mealiest smile. He knew Balboa would take the Court by storm, perhaps come back as Governor of all the Indies.

"You are hasty, son Vasco Núñez," he purred. "You do a sick old man an injustice. You accuse me as I was about to make amends. Read this."

The parchment was an appointment from King Ferdinand which conferred on Balboa the title "Adelantado (or supreme leader) of all lands bordering on the South Sea." The appointment was for life and with it was a letter thanking him for his great service to Spain.

Balboa's anger died. He would stay. He would find the murderer of his dog. Now it was possible to go on to even greater honors. There was some justice after all.

9

Adelantado of the South Sea

As Adelantado of the South Sea, Balboa was in theory
the greatest ruler of all time. In a few more years
men would know that the Pacific was larger than
the combined dry lands of the earth. But even in a
limited way the title was an empty one for King
Ferdinand had made no provision for men, supplies
or money. The monarch only suggested that Pedrarias
cooperate in every way possible.

The kind of cooperation the Governor planned to

give was immediately apparent. He sent Pizarro with ninety-three men to strip the territory around the Gulf of San Miguel. Two other parties were dispatched to plunder the adjoining coast settlements. As final insurance that Balboa would have no source of wealth Pedrarias marched out of Antigua at the head of two hundred and fifty troops and a long supply train. His destination was the group of Pearl Islands first seen by the discoverers.

Alone and without funds, Balboa started with characteristic energy to make his empty title mean something. He sketched an overland-water route that envisioned the passage of wealth from the South Sea to the ports of Spain. First he must build a city and port at Careta. There lumber and ship fittings would be assembled, then carried halfway across the Isthmus to the Balsa River. Balboa made crosses at possible sites for a shipyard far enough away from the ocean to be free of the great tides. There his fleet would be built and sailed down eighty miles to the South Sea. After that would come conquest of the Sun nation, then regular gold shipments back to Careta to be loaded into homeward-bound Spanish vessels.

To launch his dream, Balboa formed the South Sea Company, the first corporation on the American continent. Sixty old friends invested their small savings and followed the Adelantado out of Antigua.

At the kingdom of his late father-in-law, Chima, Balboa found the main village a deserted shambles. The ground, covered with the bleached skeletons of natives killed by Ayora, had been ironically christened Acla, which meant "the bones of men." On the first day Balboa marked off a plaza twice the size of the one at Antigua.

"The Adelantado," wrote Valdarrabano, "then grasped an ax and chopped down the first tree." In the days that followed Balboa did the work of five slaves as he hewed, adzed and hauled heavy timber or sweated large foundation rocks into place. The *compañeros* shrugged as they followed his example. It was true that the Spanish man-at-arms was not a slave, but who was superior to the Adelantado in any way? Everyone worked.

In less than six months Acla was the biggest city in Tierra Firme. Two hundred farmers and merchant colonists deserted Antigua for the new settlement. More people bought shares in the South Sea Company. Old settlers who had deserted Darien drifted back from Hispaniola.

A great shed was built to house the lumber from which the South Sea fleet would be built. These beams and frames were cut at Acla because it was thought that the timber there resisted the sea worm. Into the shed too went other items, hidden far in the back. Ships that laid overnight at the roadstead of Careta often sailed in the morning minus line, deadeyes, canvas, tools and even their spare anchors.

While the depot was developing Balboa sent his old lieutenants and some Negro slaves to find a building site on the Balsa and set up a way station. He made the first trip himself for the route was thought to be no longer safe. But once the natives saw their old friend, Warrior of the Sun, no Spaniard was ever harmed.

The popularity and success of the Adelantado did not help relations with Pedrarias whose expedition had been a complete failure. The Governor had been able to march inland only a few miles when he was taken ill. His loud-talking captains had met defeat from mere snipers; many men came down with fever.

Pizarro, a good enough fighting man when properly directed, also failed. The other parties, too, suffered losses. Balboa alone seemed able to attain victory.

The Adelantado's success worried Pedrarias. When he received news of King Ferdinand's death he decided it would be best to have a firm hold over Balboa lest the new King, young Charles, be impressed by stories of the strong *conquistador*. With this in mind he arranged for the engagement of his daughter Maria to Balboa. The girl was in Spain but a betrothal and marriage by proxy was a strong enough tie.

To Balboa the ritual and signing of papers meant nothing and he hoped it might get him some co-operation. To Anayansi it seemed like the loss of the man she loved, for other Indian girls had been cast off for Spanish brides.

"Before she gets here you and I will be far to the south with the *compañeros*," Balboa assured Anayansi. "You are my only wife. I swore this to your father."

The girl dried her tears. "Since that is true," she said, "I must tell you something about Andres de Garabito."

"Yes?" Balboa scowled. Garabito again. Hernan Cortes should have done more than stab the fellow.

"He says you will leave me now. That I must run off with him. If I do not, or if I tell you, I am to be cut across my face with his knife."

"I will have a talk with Garabito. He will do no cutting, *princesa mia*."

Balboa found Garabito lounging in the plaza with some friends, favorites of Pedrarias from Antigua. He wore a dagger in his belt but no sword.

"Is this thing I hear true?" Balboa demanded before Garabito could speak. "Have you bothered my wife? Did you threaten her with a knife?"

Garabito smirked. The Adelantado was unarmed so he felt safe. Balboa, he thought, would not dare insult the Governor by defending a native woman. "You speak of the savage, eh?" he asked. "Not of His Excellency's daughter?"

Balboa's left hand streaked to Garabito's belt and snagged the dagger. "You will have no need for this," he said with a wild laugh. "You are not about to fight a woman."

Quickly Balboa grabbed a handful of the man's shirt. Then he slapped him hard across the face with his calloused palm. Back and forth he slapped while Garabito swore under his breath until the pain made him cry out. Then his nose began to bleed. He sagged. Presently he was howling for mercy. He was released and soon had the knife jammed back in his belt.

"That, Garabito," said Balboa, "is the treatment for those who molest women. Next time I will treat you as a man. Do not bother my *wife* ever again."

The news reached Pedrarias the next day and a veiled rebuke followed. Balboa was advised that his shipbuilding project must be abandoned if he did not have his vessels completed and in the water before another six months had passed. It was felt that no such feat could be accomplished.

Late in August of 1517 Balboa assembled his partners, the *compañeros,* Negroes, and Indians in front of the storage shed.

"Friends," he said, "in that building are the first Spanish ships which will sail the great South Sea. When we reach the Sun kingdom you can remember that these ships have traveled by land and water."

Balboa walked to the lumber pile and lifted a four-inch plank fully half his own weight. Hoisting it to his shoulder, he headed toward the trail. Every other man then picked up his allotted fifty pounds and the unassembled ships were thus moved, single file, over the mountains to the building site one hundred miles from Acla.

The surveyors had already built shelters and ways so the keels of two small vessels were almost immediately laid under the direction of Balboa, who surprised the *compañeros* with his knowledge of the

shipwright's art. He told them of his youth at Moguer, adding: "What a man learns well in his boyhood he remembers all his life."

Web frames were set on the keels. Planks were
steamed and bent, then fastened with a few bolts
and many wooden pegs called treenails (trunnels).
The rasp of saws and the bang of hammers filled
the jungle. Then, as the craft were taking shape, disaster struck.

A cloudburst, greater than any Indian could remember, drenched the mountains and choked the
countless streams that ran into the Balsa. The river
rose twenty-five feet in a few hours. In the darkness
Balboa and his men struggled helplessly to save the
ships. But by morning everything had been destroyed.

The scene of desolation, of wasted labor, repre-
sented a test few men could pass. Little was said.
Only four months remained to get the ships launched.
Only extraordinary courage and hope could make
anyone even try. But not a man murmured. Planks
were recovered from the mud; Indians dove under
the swirling, yellow waters to salvage bolts; new
trees were felled. The Spaniards laid the keels of
two larger vessels.

In May of 1518 the *Buena Esperanza*—the Good
Hope—slid down the ways, followed by the *San*

Balboa and his men struggled in vain to save the ships

Cristobal. They were ships of about thirty tons, some thirty-five feet overall with a shallow draft and plenty of beam, for they must each carry fifty armed men into strange and possibly shoal waters.

Pilots directed the setting up of the hempen rigging and the reeving of sheets and halyards through the hardwood blocks which had been carved by Indian boys and girls. Sails were bent on the lateen yards and eighty men piled aboard for the first voyage to the South Sea.

Balboa set a course twenty-five miles off shore to the Pearl Islands. Here, away from the influence of Pedrarias, he made fast arrangements to build more ships. To sail south to the Inca Empire the Adelantado hoped to have a fleet which would carry and support two hundred and fifty men.

At the mainland headquarters a permanent establishment was set up and immediately began to attract the best men who came out from Spain. Among these was young Hernando de Soto, future discoverer of the Mississippi, then just nineteen years old. Also from home came a message: The Bishop of Seville secretly urged that Balboa make haste to explore the coast "below the equator." There was no explanation but the few words were enough, for the Bishop was one of old Fray Juan's connections.

Balboa sailed down toward what is now the port of Santa Dorothea and went ashore to pitch camp at the base of the mighty Andes mountains.

As at Darien, old men and venturesome warriors were questioned about the Inca Empire. Balboa was reminded strongly of Carlos Comogra as he heard again the tales of the Sun God who sat on a high throne made of pure gold encrusted with jewels. At some great mountain city—almost as high as heaven, it was said—the sun was caught and reflected on huge, polished shields.

The Incas used no money and there were no such things as taxes, landowning or slavery. But it was true, the old men told the Spaniards, that the Sun people held sway over many tribes who were not Incan. They did this by forcing their ways on conquered kingdoms.

Balboa heard strange accounts of artificial rivers used to irrigate the mountain plateaus. One Indian drew a sketch of a peculiar beast of burden that looked like a camel (the llama). This animal was to be seen carrying gold from the great mountains where veins of the precious metal were endless.

Afire with dreams of conquest, Balboa sailed back to the shores of San Miguel. He ordered that ships at the Pearl Islands be completed with the utmost

The conquest of Peru was at last ready to begin

speed for a rendezvous with the *Good Hope* and *San Cristobal*.

A detachment of trusted men went overland to Acla to round up hand guns, extra armor, powder and any cannon which could be bought or stolen. Balboa wished he had at his disposal the Splendid Armada which had cost King Ferdinand 54,000 pesos.

And so the conquest of Peru under the humane and gallant Balboa was ready to begin. Then fate intervened.

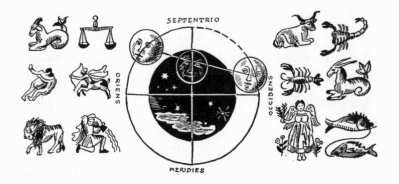

10

The Sign

In January of 1519 news reached the Pacific Coast that Pedrarias was to be replaced by Lope de Sosa, Governor of the Canary Islands. Balboa called together his partners. They met on a rainy night in his quarters and debated the best course to follow. To effect the conquest of the empire to the south they must have support from the Isthmus.

The notary, Valdarrabano, spoke first. "Now that

he is being ousted Pedrarias may try to grasp your title," he warned Balboa.

"Or Sosa may take over," Munzo suggested.

"My advice," said Arguello, "is for you to control everything, Adelantado."

"Yes, yes." Balboa raised his hands impatiently. He shook his head and frowned in concentration.

Outside the rain beat down on bamboo blinds. Those within could not see or hear the spy who leaned close, alert for just such an admission. The man slipped away and by morning was headed for Antigua. He had heard words of treason. He was already hurrying through the night when Balboa rejected the idea.

Very soon Balboa received a most cordial note from Pedrarias. Would his "son" Vasco Núñez come to Acla to talk over the new situation? Pedrarias was due to leave soon. He had not many days left on this earth and wished forgiveness for any wrong he had done. His chance lay in being able to advise his son-in-law on many matters. The Governor was sure this last wish of an ailing cavalier would not be denied.

"It is a trap, my husband," Anayansi warned. "Please! Do not go. Take one of the ships. Sail south and hide."

"You imagine things, Anayansi. The man repents.
And I will need cooperation for the conquest."

"If you won't listen to me, then read what one of
your own wise men has written. You remember him;
you befriended him. Here." Anayansi held out a
sheet of parchment.

This was the horoscope cast at Acla in the summer of 1515, on Balboa's fortieth birthday, by the
distinguished Italian, Messer Codro. A wild-eyed
scarecrow of a fellow, he had taken altitudes with
an astrolabe, consulted charts and the Signs of the
Zodiac. Balboa again read the prophecy:

> *When the stars stand this way*—the way they hap-
> pened to that night—*you will be in mortal danger.
> If you escape you will go on to be the greatest cap-
> tain of the Indies. If you are caught you will be
> destroyed.*

Balboa gently placed his hands on Anayansi's shoulders. He spoke softly: "I do not say you are wrong,
or even that the Italian was wrong. But I must go.
This is no time for me to hide. If God wills it—
not the stars—then I die. But *Santissima!*" Balboa
laughed. "Who here has the power of execution?
Only His Royal Highness commands me."

After more reassurances to Anayansi Balboa left with his men, willing to believe that Pedrarias would help him, that this meeting would be the last decent act of a sick old man who had seen the error of his ways.

The riders were approaching the way station when Balboa had his first hint of the truth. A large armed posse blocked the road. At its head, small eyes alight with hate, rode Pizarro. Balboa and his five companions were disarmed and placed in irons.

"What does this mean, Francisco Pizarro?" Balboa demanded. "Are we not old comrades-in-arms?"

"That is past, if it was ever so," Pizarro snarled. "You have held that sword for the last time. Now you will be tried for treason against His Excellency. I, for one, rejoice."

The trial was a farce. Pizarro, Garabito and every other enemy Balboa ever had, together with men he had never seen, gave false testimony in a closed session. Pedrarias gloated as Balboa was sentenced to die the next day along with Valdarrabano, Munzo, Botello and Arguello. He had drawn up many of the charges himself and had read others from a deposition written out by Encisco before the *bachiller* departed for Spain.

Among the visitors to the prison that night was Garabito, come to take even further revenge for the slapping he had received.

"Balboa," said the sly fellow, "you have a chance to save the life of that Indian girl."

"Do you mean you haven't taken Anayansi prisoner yet?"

"She was taken, along with the others. They are to be auctioned. But I had planned to look after her." Garabito leered, then his voice grew harsh. "Now she has escaped. I want to know where she is hiding."

"That I cannot tell you," Balboa said, shifting his manacles, wishing he could stand. "How did she escape?"

"She was rescued. It is said an Indian with a very long sword is responsible. The lieutenant who was disarmed and scarred swears it was an Indian. That I do not believe. No native is the match of a Spanish officer."

"As usual you are mistaken, Garabito," said Balboa. "There is one Indian swordsman in this country. Your chance of finding him, or my wife, is very much less than none." Balboa smiled in the dark. So Carlos was alive!

"I am trying to be your friend," Garabito said, turning to leave.

"Yes. I heard your lying testimony, *friend*. If you were indeed a friend you would rally the *compañeros*."

But there was no rallying of the men. The pass above Acla was blocked. Leaders aboard the invasion ships at San Miguel were placed under guard and Balboa's friends at Antigua were restrained.

Pikeman, halberdiers, cross bowmen, harquebusiers and men-at-arms, all newly arrived from Spain, dominated the crowd that gathered on the hot and sultry morning of January 15, 1519, in the plaza of Acla. All settlers were under guard.

A crier marched before the manacled Adelantado, reading off his crimes from a scroll, heralding the lie that Pedrarias was carrying out the execution order of the King against a traitor. The four companions followed their Captain. Pedrarias wet his pursed lips and squinted through a canebrake where he could watch unseen.

Balboa lifted his chained arms and called out in the familiar commanding voice:

"This is a lie, a perfidy. God is watching all of us."

Balboa made his confession, received the Sacrament and walked to the chopping block. He turned once and looked off to the south toward the lofty

In the 44th year of life Balboa went bravely to his death

mountains. What he had discovered beyond the tow-
ering range would make his name live for as long
as men record history. In the forty-fourth year of
life he went bravely to his death.

Pedrarias immediately left Acla, followed by the
black looks of every settler and Indian. His first
business was to find and appropriate Balboa's gold.
But this supposed treasure did not exist although it
was long searched for by many who could not understand that to some men deeds mean more than
gold.

The new governor, Lope de Sosa, arrived and died
aboard ship before he could land. Pedrarias then did
the unbelievable. He marched his followers to the
shore of the Pacific. While scribes wrote and wit-
nesses stood in silent embarrassment, the bitter old
man limped into the water and "discovered" the
great South Sea.

But history remembers Pedrarias only as the murderer of Balboa and many other good Spaniards,
and for the slaughter of two million natives which
earned him the nickname *Furor Domini*—The Wrath
of God.

In Mexico, where he heard of Balboa's execution,
Hernan Cortes uttered his only oath: *"St. James!"*

Later he sent an army south under the dashing Pedro de Alvarado. Meanwhile Pedrarias and his European agents were busily trying to erase the name of Balboa, hoping that posterity would forget him. His brothers Gonzaldo and Juan were shipped to South America where they were killed in battle. Later young Alvar went with Magellan, returned after half the voyage, and found it best to live quietly. For years papers and documents were hunted down and destroyed by the descendants of Pedrarias.

But the world would remember. And at the time even hardened politicians in Spain condemned the execution. They were much impressed by a strange "sign."

The sign, still on record in the Archives of the Indies at Seville, came after Pedrarias had a notice posted in the plaza of Acla. It ordered all settlers to bring their future grievances to him at his new headquarters on the shore of the ocean he had recently discovered.

Soon after the notice was posted, and while a group of men loitered in the plaza, a herd of horses came to graze near by. A favorite stallion of Balboa's left the mares. With head high he trotted across the spacious plaza. Then the big animal did something no man could explain. He stopped before the post

The horse ripped off Pedrarias's notice with his teeth

and ripped off Pedrarias's notice with his teeth. That done, he trampled the torn bits and returned to the herd.

This sign helped keep alive the fame of Vasco Núñez de Balboa.

The name South Sea appeared on charts for many years until the full extent of the ocean was realized. It then became known as the Pacific Ocean, so christened by Ferdinand Magellan in 1520 because of its calm waters.

Today in the Spanish city of Jerez de los Caballeros a street and plaza honor Balboa, the discoverer. At the Canal Zone a city named after him looks westward on the waters of the Pacific. The Republic of Panama remembers him with a decoration, a stamp and its monetary unit, which is the silver *balboa*. The coin circulates among the followers of Anayansi, Carlos, and the Indians who loved the most noble of the *conquistadores*.

Index